Decision-Making
Processes
in Pattern Recognition

ACM Monograph Series

Approximate Calculation of Integrals
by V. I. Krylov
translated by A. H. Stroud

Large-Capacity Memory Techniques for Computing Systems
edited by Marshall C. Yovits

Decision-Making Processes in Pattern Recognition
by George S. Sebestyen

Decision-Making

Processes

in Pattern Recognition

by

GEORGE S. SEBESTYEN

The Macmillan Company, New York

Macmillan New York, London

First Printing

Library of Congress catalog card number: 62-19428

The Macmillan Company, New York
Collier-Macmillan Canada, Ltd., Galt, Ontario
DIVISIONS OF THE CROWELL-COLLIER PUBLISHING COMPANY

Printed in the United States of America

Contents

1. Introduction   1

2. LINEAR METHODS IN CLASSIFICATION AND LEARNING
   2.1   Vector Representation   8
   2.2   Fundamental Assumptions   10
   2.3   Similarity and Probability   12
   2.4   Optimization and Feature Weighting   17
   2.5   Choice of an Orthogonal Coordinate System   24
   2.6   Classification, a Problem in Decision Theory   30
   2.7   Gaussian Approximation of Probability Densities   33
   2.8   Classification by Separation of Classes   37
   2.9   A Class-Separating Transformation   40
   2.10 Maximization of Correct Classifications   44
   2.11 Machine Learning and Classification   47
   2.12 Threshold Setting   51

3. NONLINEAR METHODS IN CLASSIFICATORY ANALYSIS
   3.1   Enlarging the Class of Transformations   54
   3.2   Generalized Discriminant Functions   61
   3.3   Approximation of the Generalized Discriminant   66
   3.4   An Illustrative Example   68
   3.5   Decisions Based on Incomplete Sets of Observations   74
   3.6   Recognition in Noise   80
   3.7   Decisions Based on a Finite Number of Samples   82

4. APPROXIMATE AND ADAPTIVE TECHNIQUES OF CLASSIFICATION
   4.1   A Simple Algorithm for Constructing Decision Regions   91
   4.2   Application to Speaker Recognition   93
   4.3   Algorithm for Approximating Likelihood Ratio Computations   97
   4.4   A Machine for Selective Sampling and Recognition   98
   4.5   Adaptive Sample Set Construction   99
   4.6   Application of Adaptive Sample Set Construction to Speaker Recognition   104

4.7 Bionics, Neural Nets, Adaptive Networks, and Perceptrons 108

4.8 Multilayered (Cascaded) Machines 112

5. SOME PRACTICAL PROBLEMS IN THE SOLUTION OF PATTERN RECOGNITION PROBLEMS

5.1 Geometrical Interpretation of Classification Procedures 118

5.2 Assignment of Numerical Values to Subjective Measurements 134

5.3 Selection of a Computational Procedure 139

5.4 Recognition of Voiced and Unvoiced Speech Sounds 142

5.5 Automatic Recognition of Spoken Numerals 146

Bibliography 152

Index 161

List of Illustrations

Figure

2-1.	Separation of classes	9
2-2.	Clustering by transformation	11
2-3.	Probability of membership in two categories	13
2-4.	Classification by maximum likelihood ratio	14
2-5.	Geometric interpretation of minimization	21
2-6.	Sets of transformations	29
2-7.	Separation of classes	38
2-8.	Singular class-separating transformation	42
2-9.	Elementary block diagram of the classification process	48
2-10.	Unsupervised learning	50
2-11.	Categorization	52
2-12.	Categorization with threshold	52
3-1.	Instrumentation of a class of metrics	55
3-2.	A nonlinear transformation	58
3-3.	Under transformation $u(v_1, v_2)$, F and G are separable	62
3-4.	Polynomial discriminant, $R = 1$	69
3-5.	Polynomial discriminant, $R = 2$	70
3-6.	Polynomial discriminant, $R = 3$	71
3-7.	Polynomial discriminant, $R = 4$	72
3-8.	Polynomial discriminant, $R = 6$	73
3-9.	Probability of error as a function of noise power	82
3-10.	Finite number of samples of two classes	84
3-11.	Temporary zeros of $f(v)$	85
3-12.	Modified cost structure	86
3-13.	Optimum solution $Z = 2$	87
3-14.	Optimum solution $Z = 3$	87
3-15.	Discriminant separating Gaussian processes	88
4-1.	Desired boundaries of F and G	91
4-2.	Decision regions by the "proximity rule"	92
4-3.	Model for generating "voiced" sounds	94
4-4.	Parametric representation of human speech	96

Figure

4-5. Selective sample set construction 98

4-6. Class F, the union of Gaussian processes 100

4-7. Adaptive sample set construction 103

4-8. Error probabilities as a function of the number of independent observations 107

4-9. A simple Perceptron 109

4-10. A multilayered machine 115

5-1. Decisions by maximum correlation 119

5-2. Comparison of Euclidean distances 121

5-3. The use of thresholds 122

5-4. Linear mean-square regression line 122

5-5. Classification based on proximity to nearest regression line 123

5-6. Computational simplification of classification by translation of origin and correlation 123

5-7. Illustration of shortcoming of decisions based on regression lines 124

5-8. Mean-square regression curves 126

5-9. Regression curve in N dimensions 127

5-10. Linear discriminant 128

5-11. Use of multiple discriminants 129

5-12. Nonlinear discriminant of three classes 132

5-13. Transformation of an arbitrary random variable to a Gaussian variable 135

5-14. $P(x)$ as a mapping function 136

5-15. Mapping z into a Gaussian variable 136

5-16. Mapping z into a Gaussian variable 137

5-17. Reassignment of coordinate values by use of nonlinear discriminants 138

5-18. Conventional voiced-unvoiced decision 143

5-19. Voiced-unvoiced switch 145

5-20. Sonagraph representation of the spoken word "three" 147

5-21. Confusion matrices illustrating spoken numeral recognition 150

CHAPTER 1

Introduction

As digital computers and electronic machines enter our lives in ever increasing numbers, the need for better and faster communications between man and machine becomes evident. We need machines that can be commanded by voice, machines that read print and handwriting, machines that translate from one language to another, and machines that aid in the diagnosis of diseases. As machines grow in numbers and increase in speed, their requirements for input data see no bounds. Neither does there seem to be a limit on the quantity of information that machines put out that humans must digest, comprehend, and on which they must base their decisions. From devices that retrieve from files all information that pertains to a subject of current interest to machines that aid a military commander to evaluate the threat posed by the enemy, we need machines that help us in the *use* of information thrust upon us at ever increasing rates.

As advances of modern science and technology furnish solutions to more and more complex problems, confidence is gained in the realizability of electronic machines and mathematical models that can perform these and other tasks of extreme difficulty. By and large, we declare as realizable almost any machine that must perform however difficult a task, as long as a specified set of instructions can be given stating how the task should be performed. There are problems of long-standing interest, however, that have eluded solution, partly because the problems have not been clearly defined and partly because specific instructions could not be given stating how a solution should be reached. Recognition of a spoken word independent of the speaker who utters it, recognition of a speaker regardless of the spoken text, recognition of a threat or danger in a situation in which we find ourselves, the problem of recognizing a person from his handwriting, and of distinguishing the sound of one musical instrument from that of another are only a few of the problems that have so far remained largely unsolved for reasons mentioned above. And yet these problems are solved with ease by humans in their daily lives. The emerging scientific field of pattern recognition concerns itself with the solution of these problems.

All of the above problems, however different they may seem, are united by a common bond that permits their solution with identical methods. The bond is the common requirement in the solution of these problems to possess the ability to recognize membership in classes; and even more important, the requirement for a method of establishing decision criteria for measuring membership in each class. A "specific spoken word," a "particular person's handwriting," and a "dangerous situation" are examples of classes whose members are utterances of the word by an arbitrary person, handwritten notes by a specific individual, or new dangerous situations in which we find ourselves. The task of pattern recognition consists of recognizing any such sample as a member of the class to which it belongs.

Generally speaking, no unifying concept, general theory, or common systematic approach is as yet evident in work in the field of pattern recognition. Yet, one can probably place past and present work in this field into about three groups, depending on the method employed to find a solution rather than on the class of problems whose solution is attempted.

In the first group would be placed solutions of specific problems by methods that cannot be extended to other problems in pattern recognition, except perhaps to a very few that are very similar. The now familiar method of character recognition on bank checks, T. Dimond's method of recognizing handwritten numerals, and the method of discriminating between speech and music from differences in their envelope characteristics are examples of work that could be classed in the first group. In each of these cases the successful solution of the specific problem is due to the ingenuity of a human who developed the solution. In each case the solution requires that a set of specialized measurements, specially tailored to the problem, be made on the input and that the set of measurement values agree with those listed as characterizing one or another class of interest. Recognition is thus similar to a "truth table" lookup used in switching circuits where exact or nearly exact agreement of the set of measurement values with a stored reference set is desired. The truth table describes the possible combination of measurement values for which the input is a member of the class in question.

Differences between different methods of pattern recognition are not found primarily in the form of the solution, the truth table, but rather in the manner in which entries of the truth table are obtained. In the first group entries are thought up by people rather than by machine. To borrow an appropriate phrase from Unger, in work we class in the first group, "pattern detection" is accomplished by the human, and only "pattern recognition" is done by machine. "Pattern detection" is the process of learning the characterization of a class of inputs by detecting the common pattern of attributes of inputs of the same class. "Pattern recognition" is a process of decision making in which a new input is recognized as a member of a given class by a comparison of its attributes with the *already known pattern* of common attributes of members of that class. In the discrimination between speech and music, for example, pattern detection is the research that led to the discovery and isolation of those envelope characteristics in which speech and music differ from one another. Pattern recognition is done by the device that is built to exploit these envelope differences in order to recognize sounds as originating from music or speech.

In work classed in the second group, an attempt is made to mechanize "pattern detection" by machines that learn the common attributes of inputs of a class through the simulation of the human mechanism of problem solving. The heart of the methods in this group is the specific model or block diagram that is postulated. Various models of learning and adaptive recognition systems have been studied. Each of these systems possesses certain desirable features. Such features may include the simplicity of the elements of the machine, insensitivity of machine performance to wiring errors that occur during its construction, and the distribution of memory throughout the components of the machine. These machines attempt to do pattern detection and recognition through the simulation of the human, an excellent problem solver indeed.

Methods in this group are quite general because the same methods, or the same learning model, can be applied to the solution of many different problems. Generality notwithstanding, results achieved by the first group, where learning or pattern detection is accomplished by the human, are often more noteworthy. This is to be expected since humans will be better problem solvers, for some time to come, than even the best of machines. Inputs to the models of learning in the second group of pattern recognition methods are again a set of measurements that must be performed on each sample of the classes to be recognized. The set of measurements performed on the physical world represents all the inputs on which the model operates. While the machine operates on the measurement values and learns, within the constraints of its capabilities, how to process the measurements, it remains a human task to specify what measurements should be made on the physical world. Although this question has received some attention, pattern recognition, aside from its applications, generally does not consider this problem.

A significant portion of this book falls into a third group. Here the common objective of the combined tasks of pattern detection and pattern

recognition is expressed as a solvable problem for which an optimum solution is sought. The common objective is to recognize membership in
classes, where classes are known to us only through a set of their samples. Pattern detection, the task of *learning* to recognize, consists of
finding the invariant properties of a set of samples of the class, those
properties that are common to all samples. Machine learning is thus
treated as the process of finding common properties of the physical measurements, a process which is expressible as an analytically solvable
problem. The emphasis of methods in this group is on developing automatic pattern detection and recognition techniques that achieve the recognition of new inputs with a minimum number of errors. In the discrimination of speech from music, for instance, these techniques would examine
sample speech and music envelope waveforms to determine automatically
how best to process them so that speech could be distinguished from
music with a minimum probability of error. The physical structure of the
mechanisms that achieve either pattern detection or recognition is of
secondary importance. The central problem of recognition of membership
in classes can be formulated in terms already well known. It can be considered a problem in the testing of statistical hypotheses, one that belongs in the realm of statistical decision theory.

Decision making and machine learning may be likened to a hypothetical game in which we are given two or more large sets of samples. We
are told that the first set contains a very large number of samples that
belong to the same class or category. Similarly, the second set contains
a very large number of samples of another class. We are to examine the
members of the two sets and are expected, as a result, to develop a decision procedure through which successful classification decisions can
be made. A classification decision is a choice that the decision maker
must make when he is shown a sample that was drawn from and may belong to either of two or more sets of samples. The decision maker must
determine, with a minimum probability of error, from which set the sample
was drawn. The decision theoretic processes are concerned with the development of decision rules that render classification decisions with a
minimum probability of error.

Of course, in practice, an infinite number of samples of classes are
not available. We have, instead, a finite and usually fairly small number
of samples. We must assume, at best, that these samples are representative of those that would be obtained by examining a much larger sample
size. If this requirement is satisfied — and we must usually satisfy this
requirement through engineering judgment exercised in the selection of
samples — the decision procedures that can be developed will result in
nearly the minimum number of misclassifications.

The main purpose of this book is to show the manner in which decision theoretically motivated methods can be applied to pattern-recognition

problems. It deals with the practical problems of satisfying the basic assumptions of the theory and with the changes that have to be made to mold the theory to fit the prerequisites, which in practice are not always achievable. Attention is focused on the machine learning and decision making requirements of pattern recognition problems. Other aspects of the problem not concerned with decision making or with its instrumentation are mentioned but not treated in the book.

Throughout this volume methods are considered for automatically establishing decision criteria for classifying events or things as members of one or another of the classes when the only knowledge about class membership is obtained from a finite set of their labeled samples.

Throughout this book essentially all the mathematics are developed in simple algebraic form with only occasional use of matrix notation in places where its use greatly simplifies the symbolism. Insistence on the algebraic form sometimes results in the loss of elegance and simplicity of solutions. Yet, it is felt that the ease of transition from algebra to a computer program is so significant that the loss in the aesthetic appeal of this material to a mathematician must be risked. While the mathematics are thus arithmetized and computer-oriented for practical reasons, we must not lose sight of the broader implications suggested to those well-versed in communication theory. It is a valuable mental exercise to interpret what is here presented from the point of view of communication theory. To help cross the bridge, at least partially, we may say that passing from the discrete to the continuous, from sum to integral, from dot product to correlation, and from linear transformation to passage through linear networks is generally valid in the material contained in this book. The sets of samples or events are sample functions of a random process, and the metrics developed are equivalent to using the mean-square-error criterion *after* the signal's passage through a linear network. Non-linear transformations developed to separate classes from one another are shown equivalent to generalized discriminant functions and to the computation or approximation of likelihood ratios.

The following paragraphs outline briefly the contents of this book.

First the representation of classes as multivariate random processes is developed. Each member of a class is an N-dimensional vector, where a dimension represents a physically measurable quantity. Pattern recognition is then presented as the twofold problem of learning the common properties of a set of N-dimensional vectors which represent samples of a class, and of recognizing a new vector as a possible member of the class by noting that it has properties common to those of the set of sample vectors. These two problems are interpreted using the terminology of statistical hypothesis testing. Learning is the estimation of the probability densities describing the distribution of the set of samples in the vector space, while recognition is based on the evaluation of the already learned conditional probability density of each class at the point in the vector space that represents the new input to be classified. The fundamental assumptions involved in the decision theoretical interpretation of pattern recognition problems are explained, but the method of assuring their satisfaction in practice are delayed until a later chapter.

The probability density of a class can be estimated by finding contours of equiprobable membership in the class through mathematical transformations that minimize the variance about the mean of the set of samples of the class after their transformation. It is shown that if the transformation is linear, the best fitting Gaussian probability density to members of the class is found by the above procedure.

Estimation of probability densities and the finding of generalized discriminant functions is extended by use of nonlinear techniques, following the guidelines established before. Practical problems associated with storage requirements, recognition in noise, and recognition with only partially operating equipment, are discussed. An illustration of the nonlinear techniques is given.

Approximate methods (methods that do not minimize the probability of error) and adaptive techniques of classification are discussed as a means of doing recognition less perfectly but faster and with simpler equipment than that possible with precise methods. The application of approximate methods to speaker recognition is described. A class of machines that adaptively select typical samples of a class from among a larger selection of samples is introduced. Recognition of class membership in this class of machines is based on similarity to any of the typical class samples. An illustrative application of this automatic recognition technique is presented. Neural nets, perceptron-like devices, and cascaded machines are also briefly discussed.

Practical procedures in solving pattern recognition problems with decision theoretic methods are outlined. Methods of satisfying the fundamental assumptions of the theory, the method of choosing variables of the N-variate processes representing classes, and a method of assigning numerical values to nonnumeric inputs is treated. Through an investigation of the geometric significance of various recognition techniques a better appreciation of their advantages and shortcomings is gained. The choice of recognition techniques to be applied in a practical problem is thereby facilitated. The considerations affecting practical choices and compromises are explored and illustrated with the aid of examples in which the automatic recognition of voiced versus unvoiced speech sounds and that of spoken words are discussed.

The techniques discussed in this volume have been applied to a variety of problems in addition to those given here as illustrations. A portion of this book that describes the linear methods and a part of that which deals with nonlinear methods of classification is contained in Technical Report 381 of the Research Laboratory of Electronics at the Massachusetts Institute of Technology. This report, entitled "Classification Decisions in Pattern Recognition," is based on a thesis submitted to the Department of Electrical Engineering, M.I.T., August 24, 1959, in partial fulfillment of the requirements for the degree of Doctor of Science. The research at M.I.T. was made possible in part by support extended the Massachusetts Institute of Technology, Research Laboratory of Electronics, jointly by the U.S. Army (Signal Corps), the U.S. Navy (Office of Naval Research), and the U.S. Air Force (Office of Scientific Research, Air Research and Development Command), under Signal Corps Contract DA 36-039-sc-78108, Department of the Army Task 3-99-20-001 and Project 3-99-00-000. A portion of the research was carried out under Contracts AF 30(602)-2112, and AF 30(604)-8024. Additional sponsorship was received as part of the research program of the Communication Sciences Laboratory, Data Systems Division of Litton Systems, Inc., a division of Litton Industries.

It gives me great pleasure to acknowledge my indebtedness to the staff of the Communication Sciences Laboratory where the techniques described in this volume were programmed for use with a digital computer. I am especially grateful to Dr. David Van Meter for his constructive criticisms and to Mr. Robert E. Ridley for his technical illustrations.

George S. Sebestyen

CHAPTER 2

Linear Methods in
Classification and Learning

2.1 VECTOR REPRESENTATION

The pattern recognition techniques with which we will be concerned throughout this book must perform two basic functions. First they must detect and identify the common pattern of inputs that belong to the same class, and then they must recognize this pattern in any new input to classify it as a member of one of several classes. We will be concerned chiefly with the problem of detecting the common pattern.

Since mathematical methods cannot deal with electrical signals, physical objects and optical images directly, first a mathematical model of the physical world must be constructed. We will consider that signals, images, or events to be recognized are represented by points or vectors in an N-dimensional space. Each dimension expresses a property of the event, a type of statement that can be made about it. The entire signal that represents all the information available about the event is a vector $v = (v_1, v_2, \ldots, v_N)$ the coordinates of which have numerical values that correspond to the amount of each property the event has. For instance, the photographic image of an object may be represented as a vector by scanning the photograph with a television raster and band limiting the resulting video signal. This, in effect divides the photograph into N rectangular cells. The set of cell intensities, the N equally spaced sample heights of the television video, forms an N-dimensional vector representation of the photograph. In an N-dimensional space, therefore, the entire picture can be thought of as a single point.

More generally, however, an object or event can be represented by the numerical values of a set of descriptors, by the numerical outcomes of N

quantitative tests performed on the input. Each type of test is a descriptor of the physical world, and the set of descriptors may be likened to a vocabulary of finite size to which our communication between the physical world and the machine is restricted. In this representation the set of events belonging to the same class corresponds to an ensemble of points scattered within some region of the signal space. One might expect that the set of points representing different events that belong to the same class would cluster in the N-dimensional space in the sense that "distances" between members of the same class would be small, on the average. One might also expect that members of another class would also cluster, but that the two clusters representing the two classes would remain separated from one another. A simple illustration of this idea in a two-dimensional space is shown in Fig. 2-1, where the ensemble of points,

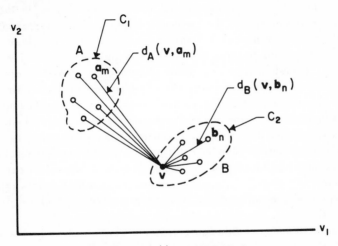

MEMBERS OF 'A' LIE WITHIN C_1,
THOSE OF 'B' LIE WITHIN C_2.

Figure 2-1. Separation of classes.

A, represents different samples of class A, and those labeled B represent samples of class B.* As is evident from the illustration, distances between points within A are smaller than those between two points, of which one is in A and the other in B. Unfortunately, this state of affairs cannot in general be expected to exist. Therefore the central problem of pattern recognition is viewed in this work as the problem of developing functions from sets of finite samples of the classes so that the functions will partition the space into regions each containing the sample points belonging to one class. The practical result to be achieved is the auto-

---

*The points a_m and b_n are the mth and nth samples of A and B, respectively.

matic construction of many dimensional templates that optimally define the regions of the N-space in which members of different classes are contained. In the two-dimensional illustration of Fig. 2-1, the areas enclosed by contours C_1 and C_2 are such templates. These templates specify how each point in the vector space should be classified. Thus the templates specify the decision rule with which membership in A or B is determined. These are areas within which members of A and B, respectively, are densely distributed.

2.2 FUNDAMENTAL ASSUMPTIONS

The concept that plays a central role *in this chapter* is the notion that, in the signal space, the ensemble of points which represents a set of nonidentical events of a common category, must be close to each other, as measured by some — as yet unknown — method of measuring distance. Transformations of the vector space or measures of distance must be developed that increase the clustering of points within a class and increase the separation between classes. This proximity requirement is significant because the points represent events that are close to each other in the sense that they are members of the same category. Mathematically speaking, the fundamental notion is that similarity (closeness in the sense of belonging to the same class or category) is expressible by a metric (a method of measuring distance) by which points representing samples of the category we wish to recognize are found to lie close to each other.

To give credence to this idea, consider what we mean by the abstract concept of a class. According to one of the possible definitions, a class is a collection of things that have some common properties. By a modification of this thought, a class could be characterized by the common properties of its members. A metric by which points representing samples of a class are close to each other must therefore operate chiefly on the common properties of the samples and must ignore, to a large extent, those properties not present in each sample. As a consequence of this argument, if a metric were found that called samples of the class close, somehow it would have to exhibit their common properties.

In order to present this fundamental idea in a slightly different way, we can state that a transformation on the signal space which is capable of clustering the points representing samples of the class must operate primarily on the common properties of the samples. A simple illustration of this idea is shown in Fig. 2-2, where the ensemble of points is spread out in the signal space (only a two-dimensional space is shown for ease

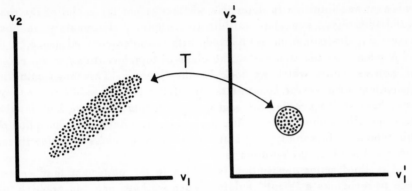

Figure 2-2. Clustering by transformation.

in illustration), but where a transformation T of the space is capable of clustering the points of the ensemble. In the example above, neither the signal's property represented by coordinate v_1 nor that represented by coordinate v_2 is sufficient to describe the class, for the spread in each is large over the ensemble of points. Some function of the two coordinates, on the other hand, would exhibit the common property that the ratio of the value of coordinate v_2 to that of coordinate v_1 of each point in the ensemble is nearly one. In this specific instance, of course, simple correlation between the two coordinates would exhibit this property; but in more general situations simple correlation will not suffice.

If the signal space shown in Fig. 2-2 were flexible (like a rubber sheet), the transformation T would express the manner in which various portions of the space must be stretched or compressed in order to bring the points together most closely. Mathematical techniques will be developed in the following that find automatically the "best" metric or "best" transformation to achieve clustering according to suitable criteria which establish "best."

As any mathematical theory, the one that results from the preceding ideas is based on certain assumptions. The first basic assumption is that the N-dimensional signal space representation of events exemplifying their respective classes is sufficiently complete to contain information about the common properties that serve to characterize the classes. The significance of this assumption is appreciated if we consider, for example, that the signal space contains all the information that a black and white television picture could present of the physical objects that constitute the samples of a class. No matter how ingenious are the data processing schemes that we might evolve, objects belonging to the category "red things" could not be identified, because representation of the samples by black and white television simply does not contain color information. For any practical situation one must rely on engineering judgment and intuition to determine whether or not the model of the real world (the signal space) is sufficiently complete. Fortunately, in most cases, this determination can be made with considerable confidence.

A second assumption states the class of transformations or the class of metrics within which we look for the "best." This assumption is equivalent to a set of constraints specifying the allowable methods of stretching or compressing the signal space within which we look for the best specific method of deforming the space. In effect, an assumption of this type specifies the type of network (such as the class of active linear networks) to which the solution is restricted.

The third major assumption is hidden in the statement that we are able to recognize a "best" solution when we have one. In practice, of course, we frequently can say what is considered a good solution even if we do not know which is the "best." The criterion by which the quality of a metric or transformation is judged good is thus one of the basic assumptions. In this work, as in statistical decision theory, the motivating criterion for judgments of "best" is that decisions be made ultimately with a minimum number of errors. The relative importance of the different kinds of errors, of course, must be taken into consideration.

The last assumption in the application of the techniques presented is that "representative" sets of samples of each of the classes of interest must be available. If the samples from which class membership is to be learned are not representative of the different types of samples that could be encountered, a distorted and incomplete view of the classes is gained, and we cannot expect to recognize all possible variations that might be observed.

2.3 SIMILARITY AND PROBABILITY

Pattern recognition consists of the two-fold task of "learning," on one hand, how to characterize the category or class to which a set of events are known to belong, and of deciding, on the other hand, whether a new event belongs to the category or not. In terms of the preceding discussion, "learning" is the task of constructing the regions or templates in the N-dimensional space in which labeled samples of the classes are contained. Recognition is the task of examining a new input and announcing the name of the region of the space in which the input is contained. In this section we consider the first of these tasks as the development of a function of any point of the space and the known set of samples so that the function, by partitioning the space into regions, will assign each point of the space to that category to which it most likely belongs. Other methods will be considered later in this chapter. A convenient and special — but not essential — way of thinking about this partitioning function is to consider it as being formed from a set of functions, one for each category. Each function measures the "probability" with which an arbitrary point of the space could be a member of the category for which the function is defined. In a sense, each function measures the similarity of an arbitrary point of the space to a given category, and the partitioning function assigns the arbitrary point to that category to which the point is most similar.

The foregoing concept of partitioning the signal space is illustrated in Fig. 2-3 where the signal space has two dimensions and the space is

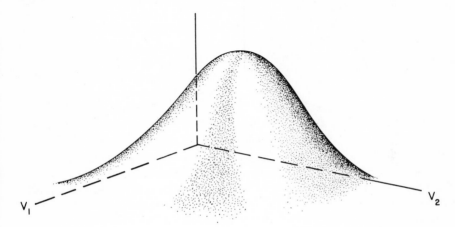

(a) Probability of membership in category 1.

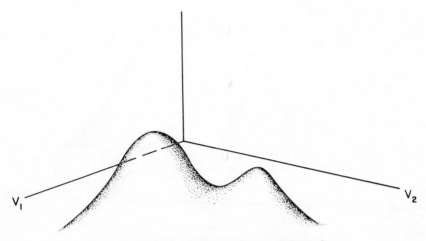

(b) Probability of membership in category 2.

Figure 2-3. Probability of membership in two categories.

to be partitioned into two categories. In Fig. 2-3(a) the height of the surface above the v_1-v_2 plane expresses the probability that points belong to Category 1, while that of the surface in Fig. 2-3(b) expresses the probability that they belong to Category 2. The intersection between the two surfaces, shown in Fig. 2-4(a) and (b), marks the boundary between Region 1, where points are more likely to belong to Category 1 than to Category 2, and Region 2, where the reverse is true.

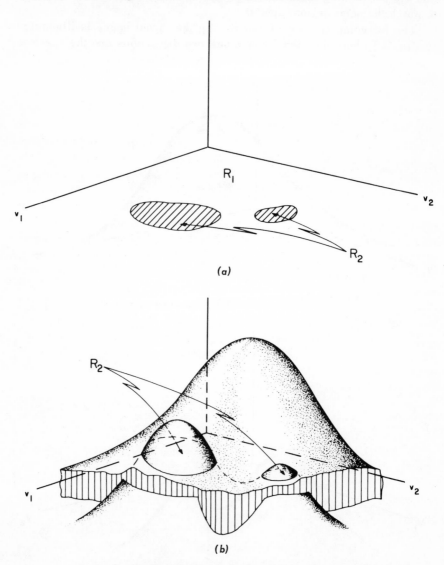

(a)

(b)

Figure 2-4. Classification by maximum likelihood ratio.

For each category of interest, a set of likelihood ratios can be computed that expresses the relative probabilities that a point in question belongs to the category of interest rather than to any of the others. From the maximum of all likelihood ratios that correspond to a given point, we may infer to which category the point *most* likely belongs.

The reader will recognize the idea of making decisions based on the maximum likelihood ratio as one of the important concepts of decision theory. This concept is briefly reviewed elsewhere in this chapter. The important fact to note in the preceding argument is that each of the surfaces in Fig. 2-3 depends only on the distribution of samples of the corresponding class. The probability of membership of a point in Category 1 depends only on the local density of samples of Category 1. It depends only on how close or similar the point is to known samples of the category; it does *not* depend on how members of *other* categories are distributed. The quantitative measure of similarity will be considered only a property of the point to be compared and the set of points that belong to the category to be learned. The *decision*, on the other hand, depends on the *relative* similarities to the different classes and does depend on members of all categories.

While decision theoretic methods base classificatory decisions on the relative degree of similarity that exists between the event to be classified and sets of samples of all the classes, one could consider methods that exploit the dissimilarities that exist between the different classes. Since the description of those properties of the samples in which two sets differ from one another is briefer, in general, than a description of *all* properties, one would expect to achieve some economy in storage and computational requirements in the former case. We will refer to methods that exploit class differences as discriminant techniques because they emphasize properties which allow discrimination between classes. Generally, discriminant techniques are inferior to those discussed previously. One would expect this on the basis of the fact that they use less information on which to base decisions. In some cases, as will be pointed out later in this chapter, they can make decisions that equal those made by likelihood ratios.

In this chapter, similarity of an event **v** to a category is measured by the closeness of **v** to every one of those events $\{f_m\}$ known to be contained in the category. Similarity S is regarded as the mean-square "distance" between **v** and the class of events represented by the set $\{f_m\}$ of its examples. The mth sample of class F is denoted by f_m.

Two things should be noted about this foregoing definition of similarity. One is that the method of measuring distance does not influence the definition. Indeed, distance is not understood here in the ordinary Euclidean sense; it may mean "closeness" in some arbitrary, abstract property of the set $\{f_m\}$ which has yet to be determined. The second thing to note is that the concept of distance between points, or distance in general, is not fundamental to a concept of similarity. The concept of "distance" is useful in that it is a real-valued function of a point and a set that allows the ordering of points according to the degree of their similarity to the set. "Distance" thus provides the ordering that "similarity" itself lacks. The concept of distance is introduced as a mathematical convenience based on intuitive notions of similarity. It will be apparent later how this concept forms part of the earlier stated assumptions as underlying the theory to be presented. Even with the introduction of the concept of distance there are other ways of defining similarity. Nearness to the closest member of the set is one such possibility. This implies that an event is similar to a class of events if it is close in some sense to any member of the class.

It is not the purpose of this chapter to philosophize about the relative merits of these different ways of defining similarity. Their advantages and disadvantages will become apparent, and the reader will be able to judge for himself which set of assumptions is most applicable under a given set of circumstances. The essential role of this definition of similarity—and the choice of the class of metrics within which the optimum is sought — is to make possible the determination of the decision rule with which membership in classes will be determined. The decision rule, of course, is not an a priori fixed rule; it contains an unknown function, the unspecified metric, which will be tailored to the particular problem to be solved. For the time being, the decision rule will remain an *ad hoc* rule; it will be shown later that it is indeed a sound rule.

To summarize the foregoing remarks, for our present purposes, similarity $S\,(\mathbf{v}, \{f_m\})$ of a point $\mathbf{v}$ and a set of points $\{f_m\}$ exemplifying a class will be defined as the mean-square distance between the point $\mathbf{v}$ and the M members of the set $\{f_m\}$. This definition is expressed by Eq. (2.1), where the metric $d(\ )$—the method of measuring distance between two points—is left unspecified.

$$S\,(\mathbf{v}, \{f_m\}) = \frac{1}{M} \sum_{m=1}^{M} d^2(\mathbf{v},\ f_m). \qquad (2.1)$$

To deserve the name metric, the function $d(\ )$ must satisfy the usual conditions stated in Eq. (2.2a), (b), (c), and (d).

$$d(\mathbf{a},\ \mathbf{b}) = d(\mathbf{b},\ \mathbf{a}) \qquad \text{(symmetric function)}; \qquad (2.2a)$$

$$d(\mathbf{a},\ \mathbf{c}) \le d(\mathbf{a},\ \mathbf{b}) + d(\mathbf{b},\ \mathbf{c}) \qquad \text{(triangle inequality)}; \qquad (2.2b)$$

$$d(\mathbf{a},\ \mathbf{b}) \ge 0 \qquad \text{(nonnegative)}; \qquad (2.2c)$$

$$d(\mathbf{a},\ \mathbf{b}) = 0 \quad \text{if, and only if,}\ \ \mathbf{a} = \mathbf{b}. \qquad (2.2d)$$

2.4 OPTIMIZATION AND FEATURE WEIGHTING

In the definition of similarity of the preceding section the mean-square distance between a point and a set of points served to measure similarity of a point to a set. The method of measuring distance, however, was left unspecified and was understood to refer to distance in perhaps some abstract property of the set. In this section the criteria for finding the "best" choice of the metric are discussed, and this optimization is applied to a specific and simple class of metrics which has interesting and useful properties.

Useful notions of "best" in mathematics are often associated with finding the extrema of the function to be optimized. We may seek to minimize the average cost of our decisions or we may maximize the probability of estimating correctly the value of a random variable. In the problem above, a useful metric, optimal in one sense, is one that minimizes the mean-square distance between members of the same set subject to certain suitable constraints devised to ensure a nontrivial solution. If the metric is thought of as extracting that property of the set in which like events are clustered, then the mean-square distance between members of the set is a measure of the size of the cluster so formed. Minimization of the mean-square distance is a method of choosing a metric that minimizes the size of the cluster and therefore extracts that property of the set in which they are most alike. It is desirable that a distance measure shall *minimize* distances between those events selected to exemplify things that are "close."

Although the preceding criterion for finding the best solution is a reasonable and meaningful assumption, it is by no means the only possibility. Minimization of the maximum distance between members of a set is just one of the possible alternatives that immediately suggests itself. It should be pointed out that ultimately the best solution is the one which results in the least number of incorrect classifications. The number of decision errors made on the known event is thus to be minimized and serves as a suitable criterion of optimization which will be dealt with elsewhere. Since our present aim is to outline a point of view regarding pattern recognition through a special example, the choice of "best" previously described and stated in Eq. (2.3) will be used, for it leads to useful solutions with relatively simple mathematics. The best metric is one that satisfies the minimization problem. In Eq. (2.3) f_p and f_m are the pth and m^{th} members of the set $\{f_m\}$:

$$\min \left[\overline{d^2(f_p, f_m)}^{p, m} \right] = \min \left[\frac{1}{M(M-1)} \sum_{m=1}^{M} \sum_{p=1}^{M} d^2(f_p, f_m) \right] \quad (2.3)$$

over all choices of $d(\ )$.

Of the many different mathematical forms that a metric may take, in the special example here described only metrics of the form given by Eq. (2.4) will be considered. Here we seek the coefficients W_n that minimize (2.3). The intuitive notions underlying the choice of the metric in this form are based on ideas of "feature weighting" which will be developed below.

$$d(\mathbf{a},\ \mathbf{b}) = \sqrt{\sum_{n=1}^{N} W_n^2 (a_n - b_n)^2}. \tag{2.4}$$

In the familiar Euclidean N-dimensional space the distance between the two points **a** and **b** is defined by Eq. (2.5). If a and b are expressed in terms of an orthonormal coordinate system $\{\theta_n\}$, then $d(\mathbf{a},\ \mathbf{b})$ of Eq. (2.5) can be written as in Eq. (2.6), where a_n and b_n, respectively, are the coordinates of **a** and **b** in the direction of θ_n.

$$d(\mathbf{a},\ \mathbf{b}) = |\mathbf{a} - \mathbf{b}|. \tag{2.5}$$

$$d(\mathbf{a},\ \mathbf{b}) = \sqrt{\sum_{n=1}^{N} (a_n - b_n)^2}. \tag{2.6}$$

We must realize that the features of the events represented by the different coordinate directions θ_n are not all equally important in influencing the definition of the category to which like events belong. Therefore it is reasonable, in comparing two points feature by feature [as expressed in Eq. (2.6)], that features with decreasing significance should be weighted with decreasing weights W_n. The idea of feature weighting is expressed by a metric somewhat more general than the conventional Euclidean metric. The modification is given in Eq. (2.7), where W_n is the feature weighting coefficient.

$$d(\mathbf{a},\ \mathbf{b}) = \sqrt{\sum_{n=1}^{N} [W_n (a_n - b_n)]^2}. \tag{2.7}$$

It is readily verified that this metric satisfies the conditions stated in Eq. (2.2) if none of the W_n is zero; if any of the W_n coefficients are zero, Eq. (2.2d) is not satisfied.

It is important to note that Eq. (2.7) gives a numerical measure of "closeness" between two points, a and b, which is strongly influenced by the particular set of similar events from which the set of W_n coefficients is computed. This is a logical result, for a measure of similarity between a and b should depend on how our notions of similarity were shaped by the events *known* to be similar. When we deal with a different set of events—the events having different "similar features" from the original set—our judgment of similarity will also be based on finding agreement between **a** and **b** among a different set of their features.

An alternative and instructive way of explaining the significance of the class of metrics given in Eq. (2.4) is to recall the analogy between metrics and transformations of the signal space. It was previously stated that the problem of expressing what is similar among a set of events of the same category is accomplished by finding *that* transformation of the signal space (again subject to suitable constraints) which will cluster most highly the transformed events in the new space. If we restrict ourselves to those linear transformations of the signal space that involve only scale-factor changes of the coordinates, and if we measure distance *in the new space* by the Euclidean metric, then the Euclidean distance between two points after their linear transformation is equivalent to the feature weighting metric of Eq. (2.4). This equivalence is shown below, where **a′** and **b′** are row vectors obtained from **a** and **b** by a linear transformation denoted by the matrix **W**. The most general linear transformation is expressed by Eq. (2.9), where a_n' is the nth coordinate of the transformed vector **a**, and b_n' is that of the vector **b**.

$$\mathbf{a} = \sum_{n=1}^{N} a_n \theta_n \qquad \text{and} \qquad \mathbf{b} = \sum_{n=1}^{N} b_n \theta_n; \qquad (2.8a)$$

$$\mathbf{a'} = \mathbf{a} \, \mathbf{W} \qquad\qquad \mathbf{b'} = \mathbf{b} \, \mathbf{W}; \qquad (2.8b)$$

$$(\mathbf{a'} - \mathbf{b'}) = (\mathbf{a} - \mathbf{b}) \, \mathbf{W}. \qquad (2.8c)$$

$$[(a_1' - b_1'), (a_2' - b_2'), \dots, (a_N' - b_N')]$$

$$= [(a_1 - b_1), (a_2 - b_2), \dots, (a_N - b_N)] \begin{bmatrix} w_{11} w_{12} \dots w_{1N} \\ w_{21} w_{22} \dots w_{2N} \\ \cdots\cdots\cdots\cdots \\ w_{N1} w_{N2} \dots w_{NN} \end{bmatrix}. \qquad (2.9)$$

The Euclidean distance between **a′** and **b′**, $d_E(\mathbf{a'}, \mathbf{b'})$, is given in Eq. (2.10).

$$d_E(\mathbf{a'}, \mathbf{b'}) = \sqrt{\sum_{n=1}^{N} (a_n' - b_n')^2} = \sqrt{\sum_{n=1}^{N} \left[\sum_{s=1}^{N} w_{ns} (a_s - b_s) \right]^2}. \qquad (2.10)$$

If the linear transformation involves only scale-factor changes of the coordinates, only the elements on the main diagonal of the **W** matrix are nonzero. The distance $d_E(\mathbf{a'}, \mathbf{b'})$ is thus reduced, in this special case, to the form given in Eq. (2.11), where w_{nn} equals the feature weighting coefficient W_n of the previous equations.

$$\text{Special } d_E(a', b') = \sqrt{\sum_{n=1}^{N} w_{nn}^{2} (a_n - b_n)^2}. \tag{2.11}$$

This particular class of metrics will be used in Eq. (2.3) to minimize the mean-square distance between the set of points.

The mathematical formulation of the minimization is given in Eq. (2.12a) and (2.12b). The significance of the constraint (2.12b) is, for the case considered, that every weight, w_{nn}, can be interpreted as the fractional value of the feature θ_n which it weights. Thus w_{nn} (a positive number between 0 and 1), denotes the fractional value assigned in the total measure of distance to the degree of agreement that exists between the components of the compared vectors.

$$\overline{D}^2 = \frac{1}{M(M-1)} \sum_{p=1}^{M} \sum_{m=1}^{M} \sum_{n=1}^{N} w_{nn}^{2} (f_{mn} - f_{pn})^2 = \text{minimum}, \tag{2.12a}$$

if

$$\sum_{n=1}^{N} w_{nn} = 1. \tag{2.12b}$$

Although the constraint of Eq. (2.12b) is appealing from a feature-weighting point of view, it leaves much to be desired. It does not guarantee, for instance, that a simple shrinkage in the size of the signal space is disallowed. Such a shrinkage would not change the relative orientation of the points to each other, the property really requiring alteration. The constraint given in Eq. (2.13), on the other hand, states that the volume of the space is constant, as if the space were filled with an incompressible fluid. Here we merely wish to determine what kind of a rectangular box could contain the space so as to minimize the mean-square distance among a set of points imbedded in the space.

$$\prod_{n=1}^{N} w_{nn} = 1. \tag{2.13}$$

The minimization problem with both of these constraints will be worked out in the following equations, and it will be seen that the results are quite similar.

Interchanging the order of summations and expanding the squared expression in Eq. (2.12a) yields Eq. (2.14), where it is recognized that the factor multiplying w_{nn}^{2} is the sample variance σ_n^{2} of the coefficients along the θ_n coordinate direction. Minimization of Eq. (2.14) under the constraint (2.12b) yields Eq. (2.15), where ρ is an arbitrary constant. Imposing constraint (2.12b) again, we can solve for w_{nn}, obtaining Eq. (2.16).

$$\overline{D^2} = \frac{M}{(M-1)} \sum_{n=1}^{N} w_{nn}^2 \left[\frac{1}{M} \sum_{m=1}^{M} f_{mn}^2 + \right.$$

$$\left. \frac{1}{M} \sum_{p=1}^{M} f_{pn}^2 - 2 \left(\frac{1}{M} \sum_{m=1}^{M} f_{mn} \right) \left(\frac{1}{M} \sum_{p=1}^{M} f_{pn} \right) \right]; \quad (2.14\text{a})$$

$$\overline{D^2} = \frac{2M}{(M-1)} \sum_{n=1}^{N} w_{nn}^2 \left(\overline{f_n^2} - \overline{f_n}^2 \right) = \frac{2M}{(M-1)} \sum_{n=1}^{N} w_{nn}^2 \sigma_n^2. \quad (2.14\text{b})$$

$$[w_{nn}\sigma_n^2 - \rho] = 0, \qquad \text{for } n = 1, 2, \ldots, N. \quad (2.15)$$

$$w_{nn} = \frac{\rho}{\sigma_n^2} = \frac{1}{\sigma_n^2 \sum_{p=1}^{N} \frac{1}{\sigma_p^2}}. \quad (2.16)*$$

That the values of w_{nn} so *found* are indeed those that minimize $\overline{D^2}$ of Eq. (2.12a) can be seen by noting that D^2 is an elliptic paraboloid in an N-dimensional space and the constraint of Eq. (2.12b) is a plane of the same dimensions. This is illustrated for a three-dimensional case in Fig. 2-5. The intersection of the elliptic paraboloid with the plane is a curve whose only point of zero derivative is a minimum.

If the variance of a coordinate of the ensemble is large, the corresponding w_{nn} is small, indicating that small weight is to be given in the

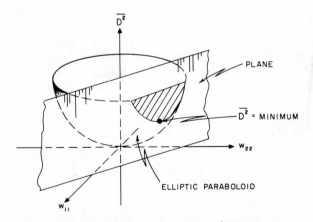

Figure 2-5. Geometric interpretation of minimization.

*Note that this result is identical with that obtained in determining the co-efficients of combination in multipath combining techniques encountered in long-distance communication systems.

measure of distance to a feature of large variation. If the variance of the magnitude of a given coordinate is small, on the other hand, then its value can be accurately anticipated; therefore the coordinate should be counted heavily in a measure of similarity. It is important to note that in the extreme case, where the variance of the magnitude of a component of the set is zero, the corresponding w_{nn} in Eq. (2.16) is equal to unity with all other w_{nn} equal to zero. In this case, although Eq. (2.11) is not a legitimate metric, since it does not satisfy Eq. (2.2), it is still a meaningful measure of similarity. If any coordinate occurs with identical magnitudes in all members of the set, it is an "all important" feature of the set and nothing else need be considered in judging the events similar. Judging membership in a category by such an "all important" feature may, of course, result in the incorrect inclusion of nonmembers into the category. For instance, "red, nearly circular figures" have the color red as a common attribute. The transformation described so far would pick out "red" as an all important feature and would judge membership in the category of "red, nearly circular figures" only by the color of the compared object. A red square, for instance, would thus be misclassified and judged to be a "red, nearly circular figure." Given only examples of the category, on the other hand, such results would probably be expected. Later in this chapter, however, where labeled examples of all categories of interest are assumed given, only those attributes are emphasized in which members of a category are alike *and* in which they differ from those of other categories.

It should be noted that the weighting coefficients do not necessarily decrease monotonically in the feature weighting that minimizes the mean-square distance among M given examples of the class. Furthermore, the results of Eq. (2.16) or (2.18) are independent of the particular ortho-normal system of coordinates; they simply state that the weighting coefficient is inversely proportional to the variance or to the standard deviation of the ensemble along the corresponding coordinate. The numerical values of the variances, on the other hand, do depend on the coordinate system.

If we use the constraint of Eq. (2.13) in place of that in (2.12b), we obtain Eq. (2.17).

$$\min \overline{D^2} = \min 2 \sum_{n=1}^{N} w_{nn}{}^2 \sigma_n{}^2, \qquad \text{for} \prod_{n=1}^{N} w_{nn} = 1; \qquad (2.17a)$$

$$\sum_{n=1}^{N} dw_{nn} \left[w_{nn} \sigma_n{}^2 - \lambda \prod_{k \neq n}^{N} w_{kk} \right] = 0. \qquad (2.17b)$$

It is readily seen that by applying Eq. (2.17a), the expression of (2.17b) is equivalent to Eq. (2.18a), where the bracketed expression must be zero for all values of n. This substitution leads to Eq. (2.18b) which may be reduced to Eq. (2.18c) by application of Eq. (2.17a) once more.

$$\sum_{n=1}^{N} dw_{nn} \left(w_{nn}\sigma_n^2 - \frac{\lambda}{w_{nn}} \right) = 0; \qquad (2.18a)$$

$$w_{nn} = \frac{\sqrt{\lambda}}{\sigma_n}; \qquad (2.18b)$$

$$w_{nn} = \left(\prod_{p=1}^{N} \sigma_p \right)^{1/N} \frac{1}{\sigma_n}. \qquad (2.18c)$$

Thus it is seen that the feature-weighting coefficient w_{nn} or W_n is proportional to the reciprocal standard deviation of the nth coordinate, thereby lending itself to the same kind of interpretation as before.

The feature weighting coefficients can be thought of as coarse descriptors of the category whose features they weight. The set of known members is the *best* description of the category. Following the practice of probability theory, this set can be described by its statistics: its ensemble mean, variance, and higher moments can be specified as the set's characteristic properties. The statistics employed by the above description of classes can be exhibited, as shown below, by simplifying the measure of similarity S of Eq. (2.1) when the specific metric of (2.11) is used.

The mean-square distance in the transformed space between a point p and members of the class F is given in Eq. (2.19a), where f_{mn} stands for the nth coordinate value of the mth sample of F. This result is obtained by substituting Eq. (2.11) into (2.1). Interchanging the order of summations, and expanding the squares yields the right hand side of Eq. (2.19a) which, through the addition and subtraction of $\overline{f_n}^2$, yields (2.19b).

$$S(\mathbf{p}, \{\mathbf{f}_m\}) = \frac{1}{M} \sum_{m=1}^{M} \sum_{n=1}^{N} w_{nn}^2 (p_n - f_{mn})^2 =$$

$$\sum_{n=1}^{N} w_{nn}^2 \left[p_n^2 - 2p_n\overline{f_n} + \overline{f_n^2} \right]; \qquad (2.19a)$$

$$= \sum_{n=1}^{N} w_{nn}^2 \left[(p_n - \overline{f_n})^2 + \sigma_n^2 \right] =$$

$$\sum_{n=1}^{N} w_{nn}^2 (p_n - \overline{f_n})^2 + K. \qquad (2.19b)$$

If w_{nn} from Eq. (2.18) is substituted into the quadratic form of Eq. (2.19), Eq. (2.20) is obtained.

$$S(\mathbf{p}, \{\mathbf{f}_m\}) = \lambda \left[\sum_{n=1}^{N} \left(\frac{p_n - \overline{f_n}}{\sigma_n} \right)^2 + N \right] =$$

$$\left(\prod_{p=1}^{N} \sigma_p \right)^{2/N} \left[\sum_{n=1}^{N} \left(\frac{p_n - \overline{f_n}}{\sigma_n} \right)^2 + N \right]. \qquad (2.20)$$

Contours of constant $S(\mathbf{p}, \{\mathbf{f}_m\})$ are ellipses centered at $\overline{\mathbf{f}}$, where $\overline{\mathbf{f}}$ is the sample mean, and the semiaxes of the ellipses are the variances of the samples in the directions of the coordinate axes.

It may be seen that the category can be described by first and second order statistics of the given samples. This fact also reveals the limitations of the particular class of metrics considered above, for there are classes for which first and second order statistics are not sufficient descriptors. It should be pointed out, however, that this is a limitation of the particular, restricted class of metrics just considered, rather than a limitation of the approach used.

2.5 CHOICE OF AN ORTHOGONAL COORDINATE SYSTEM

Labeled events that belong to a category have been assumed given as vectors in an assumed coordinate system that expressed features of the events thought to be relevant to the description of the category. An optimum set of feature weighting coefficients through which similar events could be judged most similar to one another was then found. It would be purely coincidental, however, if the features represented by the given coordinate system were optimal in expressing the similarities among members of the set. In this section, therefore, we look for a new set of coordinates, spanning the same space and expressing a different set of features that minimize the mean-square distance between members of the set. The problem just stated can be thought of as either enlarging the class of metrics considered thus far in the measure of similarity defined earlier, or as enlarging the class of transformations of the space within which class we look for that particular transformation that minimizes the mean-square distance between similar events.

It was proved earlier that the linear transformation that changes the scale of the nth dimension of the space by the factor w_{nn} while keeping the volume of the space constant and minimizing the mean-square distance between the transformed vectors is given by Eq. (2.22).

$$f' = f W \quad W = \begin{bmatrix} w_{11} & & & & 0 \\ & w_{22} & & & \\ & & \cdot & & \\ & & & \cdot & \\ & & & & \cdot \\ 0 & & & & w_{NN} \end{bmatrix} ; \qquad (2.22a)$$

and

$$w_{nn} = \left(\prod_{p=1}^{N} \sigma_p \right)^{1/N} \frac{1}{\sigma_n} . \qquad (2.22b)$$

The mean-square distance under this transformation is a minimum for the given choice of orthogonal coordinate system. It is given by

$$\min \overline{D^2} = \frac{1}{M(M-1)} \sum_{p=1}^{M} \sum_{m=1}^{M} \sum_{n=1}^{N} w_{nn}^2 (f_{mn} - f_{pn})^2. \qquad (2.23)$$

It is possible, however, to rotate the coordinate system until one is found that minimizes this minimum mean-square distance. While the first minimization took place with respect to all choices of the w_{nn} coefficients, we are now interested in further minimizing $\overline{D^2}$ by first rotating the coordinate system so that the above optimum choice of the w_{nn} should result in the absolute minimum distance between vectors.* The solution of this search for the optimum transformation can be conveniently stated in the form of the following theorem.

THEOREM

The orthogonal transformation which minimizes the mean-square distance between a set of vectors, subject to the constraint that the volume of the space is invariant under transformation, is a rotation C followed by a diagonal transformation W. The rows of the matrix C are eigenvectors of the covariance matrix U of the set of vectors, and the elements of W are those given in Eq. (2.22b), where σ_p is the standard deviation of the coefficients of the set of vectors in the direction of the pth eigenvector of U.

PROOF

Expanding the square of Eq. (2.23) and substituting the values of w_{nn} result in Eq. (2.24) which is to be minimized over all choices of the coordinate system.

---

*This sequence of operations leads to results identical to those we would obtain by solving for the whole matrix in one operation.

$$\overline{D^2} = \frac{1}{M(M-1)} \sum_{n=1}^{N} w_{nn}^2 \sum_{p=1}^{M} \sum_{m=1}^{M} (f_{mn}^2 + f_{pn}^2 - 2f_{mn}f_{pn}); \quad (2.24a)$$

$$= \frac{2M}{(M-1)} \sum_{n=1}^{N} w_{nn}^2 \left(\overline{f_n^2} - \overline{f_n}^2 \right) = \frac{2M}{(M-1)} \sum_{n=1}^{N} w_{nn}^2 \sigma_n^2; \quad (2.24b)$$

$$= \frac{2M}{(M-1)} \sum_{n=1}^{N} w_{nn}^2 \sigma_n^2 = \frac{M}{(M-1)} 2N \left[\prod_{p=1}^{N} \sigma_p^2 \right]^{1/N}. \quad (2.24c)$$

Let the given coordinate system be transformed by the matrix $\mathbf{C}$;

$$\mathbf{C} = \begin{bmatrix} c_{11} & c_{12} \cdots c_{1N} \\ c_{21} & c_{22} \cdots c_{2N} \\ \cdots \cdots \cdots \\ c_{N1} & c_{N2} \cdots c_{NN} \end{bmatrix}, \text{ where } \sum_{n=1}^{N} c_{pn}^2 = 1,^* \quad p = 1, 2, \ldots, N. \quad (2.25)$$

Equation (2.24) is minimized if the bracketed expression in Eq. (2.24c), which we shall name β, is minimized.

$$\beta = \prod_{p=1}^{N} \sigma_p^2 = \prod_{p=1}^{N} \left[\frac{1}{M} \sum_{m=1}^{M} (f'_{mp})^2 - \left(\frac{1}{M} \sum_{m=1}^{M} f'_{mp} \right)^2 \right], \quad (2.26a)$$

where

$$f'_{mp} = \sum_{n=1}^{N} f_{mn} c_{pn}. \quad (2.26b)$$

Substituting Eq. (2.26b) into Eq. (2.26a), we obtain

$$\beta = \prod_{p=1}^{N} \left[\sum_{n=1}^{N} \sum_{s=1}^{N} \frac{1}{M} \sum_{m=1}^{M} f_{mn} f_{ms} c_{pn} c_{ps} - \left(\sum_{n=1}^{N} \overline{f_n} c_{pn} \right)^2 \right], \quad (2.27)$$

in which the averaging is understood to be over the set of M vectors. The squared expression may be written as a double sum and the entire equation simplified to

$$\beta = \prod_{p=1}^{N} \sum_{n=1}^{N} \sum_{s=1}^{N} (\overline{f_n f_s} - \overline{f_n}\,\overline{f_s}) \, c_{pn} c_{ps}. \quad (2.28)$$

---

*The transformation defined by the matrix $\mathbf{C}$ is more general than an orthogonal matrix. It includes orthogonal matrices as a special case. The choice of this constraint will be discussed at the end of section 2.5.

But $\overline{(f_n f_s} - \overline{f_n} \overline{f_s}) = u_{ns} = u_{sn}$ is an element of the covariance matrix **U**. Hence we have

$$\beta = \prod_{p=1}^{N} \sum_{n=1}^{N} \sum_{s=1}^{N} u_{ns} c_{pn} c_{ps}. \qquad (2.29)$$

Using the method of Lagrange multipliers to minimize β in Eq. (2.29), subject to the constraint of Eq. (2.25), we obtain Eq. (2.30) as the total differential of β. The differential of the constraint γ is given in Eq. (2.31).

$$d\beta(c_{11} c_{12} \cdots c_{NN})$$

$$= \sum_{l=1}^{N} \sum_{q=1}^{N} \left[\prod_{p \neq l}^{N} \sum_{n=1}^{N} \sum_{s=1}^{N} u_{ns} c_{pn} c_{ps} \right] \frac{\partial}{\partial c_{lq}} \times$$

$$\left(\sum_{a=1}^{N} \sum_{b=1}^{N} u_{ab} c_{la} c_{lb} \right) dc_{lq}. \qquad (2.30)$$

$$d\gamma_l = 2 \sum_{q=1}^{N} c_{lq} dc_{lq} \qquad l = 1, 2, \ldots, N \qquad (2.31)$$

By way of an explanation of Eq. (2.30), note that when Eq. (2.29) is differentiated with respect to c_{lq}, all of the factors in the product in Eq. (2.29), where $p \neq l$, are simply constants. Carrying out the differentiation stated in Eq. (2.30), we obtain

$$d\beta = 2 \sum_{l=1}^{N} \sum_{q=1}^{N} dc_{lq} \left[\sum_{b=1}^{N} c_{lb} u_{qb} \right] \prod_{p \neq l}^{N} \left[\sum_{n=1}^{N} \sum_{s=1}^{N} u_{ns} c_{pn} c_{ps} \right]. \qquad (2.32)$$

Now let

$$\prod_{p \neq l}^{N} \sum_{n=1}^{N} \sum_{s=1}^{N} u_{ns} c_{pn} c_{ps} = A_l \qquad (2.33)$$

and note that since $p \neq l$, A_l is just a constant as regards optimization of any c_{lx}.

In accordance with the method of Lagrange multipliers, each of the N constraints of Eq. (2.31) is multiplied by a different arbitrary constant B_l and is added to $d\beta$ as shown below.

$$d\beta = \sum_{l=1}^{N} B_l d\gamma_l = 0 = 2 \sum_{l=1}^{N} \sum_{q=1}^{N} dc_{lq} \left[\left(\sum_{b=1}^{N} c_{lb} u_{qb} \right) A_l + B_l c_{lq} \right]. \qquad (2.34)$$

By letting $-\lambda_l = B_l / A_l$ and by recognizing that dc_{lq} is arbitrary, we get

$$\sum_{b=1}^{N} c_{lb} u_{qb} - \lambda_l c_{lq} = 0 \qquad q = 1, 2, \ldots, N; \qquad l = 1, 2, \ldots, N. \tag{2.35}$$

Let the lth row of the C matrix be the vector c_l. Then Eq. (2.35) can be written as the eigenvalue problem of Eq. (2.36) by recalling that $u_{qb} = u_{bq}$.

$$c_l (\mathbf{U} - \lambda_l \mathbf{I}) = 0 \qquad l = 1, 2, \ldots, N. \tag{2.36}$$

Solutions of Eq. (2.36) exist only for N specific values of λ_l. The vector c_l is an eigenvector of the covariance matrix $\mathbf{U}$. The eigenvalues λ_l are positive, and the corresponding eigenvectors are orthogonal, since the matrix $\mathbf{U}$ is positive definite. Since the transformation $\mathbf{C}$ is to be nonsingular, the different rows c_l must correspond to different eigenvalues of $\mathbf{U}$. It may be shown that the only extremum of β is a minimum, subject to the constraint of Eq. (2.25). Thus the optimum linear transformation that minimizes the mean-square distance of a set of vectors while keeping the volume of the space constant is given by Eq. (2.37), where rows of $\mathbf{C}$ are eigenvectors of the covariance matrix $\mathbf{U}$.

$$
\begin{bmatrix}
a_{11} a_{12} \cdots a_{1N} \\
a_{21} a_{22} \cdots a_{2N} \\
\cdots \cdots \cdots \cdots \\
a_{N1} a_{N2} \cdots a_{NN}
\end{bmatrix}
=
\begin{bmatrix}
c_{11} c_{12} \cdots c_{1N} \\
c_{21} c_{22} \cdots c_{2N} \\
\cdots \cdots \cdots \cdots \\
c_{N1} c_{N2} \cdots c_{NN}
\end{bmatrix}^{T}
\begin{bmatrix}
w_{11} & & & \\
& w_{22} & & \\
& & \cdot & \\
& & & \cdot \\
& & & & w_{NN}
\end{bmatrix}
$$

$$
=
\begin{bmatrix}
w_{11} c_{11} & w_{22} c_{21} \cdots w_{NN} c_{N1} \\
w_{11} c_{12} & w_{22} c_{22} \cdots w_{NN} c_{N2} \\
\cdots \cdots \cdots \cdots \cdots \cdots \\
w_{11} c_{1N} & w_{22} c_{2N} \cdots w_{NN} c_{NN}
\end{bmatrix}. \tag{2.37}
$$

The numerical value of the minimum mean-square distance may now be computed as follows. The quantity $\overline{D^2}$ was given in Eq. (2.24c), which is reproduced here as Eq. (2.38):

$$\overline{D^2} = \frac{M}{(M-1)} 2N \left[\prod_{p=1}^{N} \sigma_p^2 \right]^{1/N} = \frac{M}{(M-1)} 2N (\beta)^{1/N}. \tag{2.38}$$

Substituting β from Eq. (2.29), we obtain

$$\overline{D^2} = \frac{M}{(M-1)} 2N \left[\prod_{p=1}^{N} \sum_{n=1}^{N} \sum_{s=1}^{N} u_{ns} c_{pn} c_{ps} \right]^{1/N} \tag{2.39}$$

But from Eq. (2.35) we see that min $\overline{D^2}$ may be written as

$$\min \overline{D^2} = \frac{M}{(M-1)} 2N \left[\prod_{p=1}^{N} \sum_{n=1}^{N} \lambda_p c_{pn}^2 \right]^{1/N} =$$

$$\frac{M}{(M-1)} 2N \left(\prod_{p=1}^{N} \lambda_p \right)^{1/N}, \qquad (2.40)$$

in which the constraint of Eq. (2.25) has been used.

It should be noted that the constraint of Eq. (2.25) is not, in general, a constant volume constraint. Instead, the constraint holds the product of the squared lengths of the sides of all N-dimensional parallelepipeds a constant. If, as in the solution just obtained, the transformation C turns out to be orthogonal, the volume is maintained constant. A subset of the constant volume transformations, T_v (Fig. 2-6), are the orthogonal transformations T_0 of constant volume of which the optimum was desired. The solution presented here found the optimum transformation among a set of T_L that contains orthogonal transformations of constant volume but is not necessarily constant volume for those that are non-orthogonal. The solution given here, therefore, is optimum among the constant volume transformations $T_v \cap T_L$ shown as the shaded area in Fig. 2-6. This intersection is a larger set of transformations than that for which the optimum was sought.

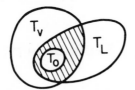

Figure 2-6. Sets of transformations.

The methods discussed in this section are optimal in measuring membership in classes of certain types. In the next section, where a decision theoretical interpretation of classification is given, the specific classes for which these methods are optimum will be stated. First, however, the important points discussed thus far will be summarized.

Categorization, the basic problem of pattern recognition, is regarded as the process of learning how to partition the signal space into regions where each contains points of only one category. The notion of similarity between a point and a set of points of a category plays a dominant role in the partitioning of signal space. Similarity of a point to a set of points is regarded as the mean-square "distance" between the point and the set. The sense in which distance is understood is not fully specified, but the optimum sense is understood to be that which (by the optimum method of measuring distance) clusters most highly those points that belong to the same category. The mean-square distance between points of a category is a measure of clustering. An alternate interpretation of similarity is that the transformation that optimally clusters like points, subject to suitable constraints ensuring the nontriviality of the transformations, is instrumental in exhibiting the similarities between points of a set. In particular, the optimum orthogonal transformation, and a non-Euclidean method of measuring distance on the original space is found that minimizes the mean-square distance between a set of points, if the volume of the space is held constant to ensure nontriviality. The resulting measure of similarity between a point $\mathbf{p}$ and a set $\{\mathbf{f}_m\}$ is

$$S(\mathbf{p}, \{\mathbf{f}_m\}) = \frac{1}{M} \sum_{m=1}^{M} \sum_{n=1}^{N} \left[\sum_{s=1}^{N} a_{ns}(p_s - f_{ms}) \right]^2, \qquad (2.41)$$

where a_{ns} is given in the theorem of this section.

Classification of an arbitrary point $\mathbf{p}$ into one of two categories, F or G, is accomplished by the decision rule given in Eq. (2.42), where the functions S_f and S_g are obtained from samples of F and samples of G, respectively.

$$\text{Decide } \mathbf{p} \in F, \text{ if } S_f(\mathbf{p}, \{\mathbf{f}_m\}) < S_g(\mathbf{p}, \{\mathbf{g}_m\}),$$
$$\text{decide } \mathbf{p} \in G, \text{ if } S_f(\mathbf{p}, \{\mathbf{f}_m\}) > S_g(\mathbf{p}, \{\mathbf{g}_m\}). \qquad (2.42)$$

2.6 CLASSIFICATION, A PROBLEM IN DECISION THEORY

The decision procedures discussed in the preceding sections are motivated by decision theory. We will briefly outline some of the principles of that theory to make the relationship clear and to bridge the gap between the geometric notions of preceding sections and the mathematically precise terms of statistical decision theory.

Consider the situation in which an arbitrary event represented by the N-dimensional vector $\mathbf{v} = (v_1, v_2, \ldots, v_N)$ may be a member of only one or two classes F or G. We would like to develop a decision procedure that could examine the input, $\mathbf{v}$, and decide, with a minimum probability of error, of which of the classes, F or G, $\mathbf{v}$ is most likely a member. In developing a decision procedure, we must recognize, of course, that two kinds of decision errors can be made. We can sound a false alarm by deciding that $\mathbf{v}$ is a member of class F when it is indeed not; or we can falsely dismiss $\mathbf{v}$ as not a member of F when indeed it is. These two kinds of errors, false alarms or false dismissals, are sometimes not equally important to the decision maker. In an important practical application, for instance, class F may stand for "underwater sound signals caused by a passing submarine" while class G may stand for "underwater sounds *not* caused by submarines." It is readily appreciated that different weight may be given a false alarm (calling a signal a submarine sound when it is not) than a false dismissal (rejecting a submarine sound as one not caused by submarines). The two weights are often determined on the basis of the cost of the two kinds of errors to the decision maker. We will refer to them as the cost of alarm, c_a, and that of dismissal, c_d.

Ultimately the decision procedure or rule must be able to define a decision for each point in the N-space. Each input must be, in the above simple example, either of class F or of class G. Now suppose that we know the probability with which the particular combination of observations $\mathbf{v} = (v_1, v_2, \ldots, v_N)$ will occur, under the condition that we are told that $\mathbf{v}$ is a member of F. This probability reflects on the relative density of members of F in the neighborhood of the point $\mathbf{v}$ and is therefore called the conditional probability density of class F, $p(v_1, v_2, \ldots, v_N|F)$. Given that F occurred, this is the numerical value of the probability of observing $v_1, v_2, \ldots, v_N$. Similarly, assume that the conditional probability density $p(v_1, v_2, \ldots, v_N|G)$ is also known. These two functions were graphically illustrated in Fig. 2-3. The probability of false alarm (of deciding F when G occurred) may now be written as the total probability of finding $\mathbf{v}$ in the region R_F, where we decide that inputs are members of F. Note that the probability of an alarm is the probability of $\mathbf{v}$ falling in R_F, given that $\mathbf{v}$ belongs to G, *times* the probability, $P(G)$, that G occurs in the first place. $P(G)$ is called the *a priori* probability of G, its probability of occurrence before measurements on the input are taken. For instance, G may occur three times as frequently as F, causing $P(G) = 0.75$, $P(F) = 0.25$.

$$P(\text{alarm}) = P(G) \int \cdots \iint_{R_F} p(v_1, v_2, \ldots, v_N|G)\,dv_1 dv_2 \ldots dv_N. \qquad (2.43)$$

Similarly, the probability of false dismissal is the total probability that we observe a member of F in the region R_G in which we decide that G occurred.

$$P(\text{dismissal}) = P(F) \int \cdots \iint_{R_F} p(v_1, v_2, \ldots, v_N|F)\,dv_1 dv_2 \ldots dv_N. \qquad (2.44)$$

In many cases, a wise decision maker, according to the fundamental premise of statistical decision theory, will use a rule that minimizes the "Risk," or average "cost" of decision making. The risk is given in Eq. (2.45) as the cost of alarm and dismissal, on the average.

$$\text{Risk} = c_a P(\text{alarm}) + c_d P(\text{dismissal}). \tag{2.45}$$

Substituting (2.43) and (2.44) into Eq. (2.45), and recognizing that the integral of a probability density over both R_F and R_G (over the whole space) is unity, we obtain Eq. (2.46).

$$\text{Risk} = c_a P(F)$$
$$+ \int \cdots \iint_{R_F} \Big[c_a P(G) p(v_1, v_2, \ldots, v_N | G) - \tag{2.46}$$
$$c_d P(F) p(v_1, v_2, \ldots, v_N | F) \Big] dv_1, dv_2, \ldots, dv_N.$$

The objective of the decision maker is to partition the N-space into two regions R_F and R_G so that the risk, Eq. (2.46), is minimized. Note that R_G is just the complement of R_F. The decision maker must choose R_F so that the integral is most negative. Clearly, this can be achieved if R_F is chosen so that the integrand is always negative and if no region where the integrand is negative is outside R_F. This is expressed by the inequality of Eq. (2.47a) or (b) where

$$c_a P(G) p(v_1, v_2, \ldots, v_N | G) - c_d P(F) p(v_1, v_2, \ldots, v_N | F) < 0 \tag{2.47a}$$

$$\therefore \text{ decide } v \in F \text{ if } \frac{p(v_1, v_2, \ldots, v_N | F)}{p(v_1, v_2, \ldots, v_N | G)} > \frac{c_a P(G)}{c_d P(F)} = T. \tag{2.47b}$$

the costs and a priori probabilities are constants. Thus the decision rule that minimizes risk compares the ratio of two probability densities with a threshold value T to decide if v is most likely a member of F or of G. The ratio of probability densities is called the "likelihood ratio" and the class of decision rules, Bayes' rules. In the simple case where the costs and a priori probabilities are equal ($T = 1$), the optimum decision consists of determining whether the set of observations are more likely under the assumption that they were caused by an event of class F than by an event of class G.

An important fact in the above decision procedure is that the numerical values associated with costs and prior probabilities do not influence the nature of the computations one must perform on the input. They merely influence the threshold of comparison. Another fact to note is that besides problems of classificatory decision a number of different kinds of decision problems can be formulated in the above terms. In classical detection problems, for instance, F stands for the "signal plus noise" population of vectors that arise from measurements taken on a noisy observation of a specific waveform. In this problem G stands for the population of waveforms arising from "noise alone." Thus we deal with the optimum detection of signals in noise.

There are principally two factors that limit the usefulness of the theory developed along these directions. The first is the assumption that the conditional joint probability densities are known. In some cases this is indeed possible, particularly if we know the physical processes that generate the F and G populations of signals. We may know, for instance, that F and G are two specific signal waveforms immersed in Gaussian noise of known description. More often than not, however, we have no knowledge of the generating process; indeed one of our aims is to try to describe it. In principle, at least, we can always obtain the probability densities by observing the relative frequency with which each of the possible combinations of N measurement values occurs as the number of samples of the class on which the observations are made approaches infinity. Except in very rare instances, this, of course, is not a practical method of constructing the probability densities. Most often one has to be satisfied with a finite and usually fairly small number of samples from which to estimate the unknown densities. The task of learning, in pattern recognition, can be thought of as that of estimating the densities that describe the distribution of samples in the vector space. Recognition, on the other hand, is based on the evaluation of the already learned conditional probability density of each class at the point in the vector space that represents the new input to be classified These two facets of the problem are approached in this volume alternately from a geometrical and a decision theoretic point of view. We assume throughout the discussions that available samples of the classes are representative of the classes; that is, the samples are distributed as if they were randomly drawn from the infinite population of samples. Thus we assume that probability densities constructed from samples are similar to the true probability densities.

A second factor that limits the usefulness of decision theory is the constraints imposed on the realizability of the decision rule. If the probability densities are not analytically expressible, even if they are known to us, their values at each point in the N-space must be stored and tabulated. The resulting storage requirements prohibit the realization of likelihood ratio computers in all but the simplest cases. We must thus search for methods that analytically approximate the likelihood ratio computer or otherwise limit the storage requirements. The methods discussed herein attempt both.

2.7 GAUSSIAN APPROXIMATION OF PROBABILITY DENSITIES

If the actual probability densities are approximated by analytic expressions of an often occurring random process, decisions based on likelihood ratios and those made by the decision rule developed earlier in this chapter are identical. If samples of each class are generated by Gaussian processes with unknown but, in general, different means and variances, then, it will be shown, the measure S of this chapter measures contours of constant probability density. A comparison of the logarithm of the likelihood ratio with a constant threshold will be shown equal to the decision rule of Eq. (2.42).

Let us examine the joint probability density $p(v_1, v_2, \ldots, v_N | F)$ denoted by $p_F(v_1, v_2, \ldots, v_N)$ or $p_F(\mathbf{v})$. For the multivariate Gaussian process the joint probability density is given by Eq. (2.48), where $\mathbf{U}$ is the covariance matrix of F and $[U_{rs}]$ is the cofactor of the element with like subscripts in the covariance matrix. It should be noted that $[U_{rs}]/|\mathbf{U}|$ is an element of $\mathbf{U}^{-1}$.

$$p_F(v_1, v_2, \ldots, v_N) =$$

$$= \frac{1}{(2\pi)^{N/2}|\mathbf{U}|^{1/2}} \exp\left[-\frac{1}{2}\sum_{r=1}^{N}\sum_{s=1}^{N}\frac{[U_{rs}]}{|\mathbf{U}|}(v_r - m_r)(v_s - m_s)\right] \qquad (2.48a)$$

$$= \frac{1}{(2\pi)^{N/2}|\mathbf{U}|^{1/2}} \exp\left[-\frac{1}{2}\sum_{r=1}^{N}\sum_{s=1}^{N}U_{rs}^{-1}(v_r - m_r)(v_s - m_s)\right]. \qquad (2.48b)$$

Contours of constant joint probability density occur for those values of $\mathbf{v}$ for which the argument of the exponential is constant. The exponent expressed in matrix notation is

$$\text{exponent} = \text{constant} = \left[-\frac{1}{2}(\mathbf{v} - \mathbf{m}_v)\,\mathbf{U}^{-1}(\mathbf{v} - \mathbf{m}_v)^T\right], \qquad (2.49)$$

where $\mathbf{m}_v$ is the mean vector of class F in the v coordinate system.

We recall from the theorem of this chapter that one of the operations on the set of points $\{\mathbf{f}_m\}$ which the optimum metric performed was a rotation expressible by an orthogonal matrix $\mathbf{C}$. This is a pure rotation (an orthonormal transformation), where columns of $\mathbf{C}$ are unit eigenvectors of the covariance matrix $\mathbf{U}$. This will aid in the establishment of the relation between the exponent of the Gaussian density and the measure S.

Let $\mathbf{y}$ be a new variable obtained from $\mathbf{v}$ by Eq. (2.50). Substituting Eq. (2.50) in Eq. (2.49), we obtain Eq. (2.51).

$$\mathbf{y} = \mathbf{v}\mathbf{C}; \qquad (2.50a)$$

$$\mathbf{v} = \mathbf{y}\mathbf{C}^{-1}; \qquad (2.50b)$$

$$\text{exponent} = \left[-\frac{1}{2}(\mathbf{y} - \mathbf{m}_y)\,\mathbf{C}^{-1}\mathbf{U}^{-1}(\mathbf{C}^{-1})^T(\mathbf{y} - \mathbf{m}_y)^T\right], \qquad (2.51)$$

where $\mathbf{m}_y$ is the mean vector of F in the y coordinate system.

Since $\mathbf{C}$ is orthogonal, the special property of orthogonal matrices that $\mathbf{C}^{-1} = \mathbf{C}^T$ can be used to simplify Eq. (2.51). This yields

$$\text{exponent} = \left[-\frac{1}{2}(\mathbf{y} - \mathbf{m}_y) \, \mathbf{C}^T\mathbf{U}^{-1}\mathbf{C} \, (\mathbf{y} - \mathbf{m}_y)^T \right]. \qquad (2.52)$$

Furthermore, since columns of $\mathbf{C}$ are eigenvectors of the covariance matrix $\mathbf{U}$, the matrix $\mathbf{C}$ must satisfy Eq. (2.53a), where Λ is the diagonal matrix of eigenvalues of $(\mathbf{U} - \lambda_n\mathbf{I}) = 0$.

$$\mathbf{C}^T(\mathbf{U} - \Lambda) \, \mathbf{C} = 0; \qquad \mathbf{C}^T\mathbf{U}\mathbf{C} = \mathbf{C}^T\Lambda\mathbf{C} = \Lambda. \qquad (2.53a)$$

$$\Lambda = \begin{bmatrix} \lambda_1 & & & & 0 \\ & \lambda_2 & & & \\ & & \cdot & & \\ & & & \cdot & \\ 0 & & & & \lambda_N \end{bmatrix}. \qquad (2.53b)$$

By taking the inverse of both sides of Eq. (2.53a) and again employing the special property of orthogonal matrices, Eq. (2.54) may be obtained. This expression, when substituted in Eq. (2.52) produces the result stated in Eq. (2.55).

$$\mathbf{C}^T\mathbf{U}^{-1}\mathbf{C} = \Lambda^{-1}. \qquad (2.54)$$

$$\text{Exponent} = \text{constant} = \left[-\frac{1}{2}(\mathbf{y} - \mathbf{m}_y) \, \Lambda^{-1}(\mathbf{y} - \mathbf{m}_y)^T \right]. \qquad (2.55)$$

The quadratic form of Eq. (2.55) expresses the fact that contours of constant probability density are ellipsoids with centers at $\mathbf{m}_y$, the direction of the principal axes is along eigenvectors of the covariance matrix, and the diameters are equal to the corresponding eigenvalues. Converting the quadratic form of Eq. (2.55) to a sum in Eq. (2.56) exhibits this result in a more familiar form, where y_n is the coordinate of $\mathbf{y}$ in the direction of the nth eigenvector and m_n is the mean of the ensemble in the same direction.

$$\text{Exponent} = \left[-\frac{1}{2} \sum_{n=1}^{N} \frac{(y_n - m_n)^2}{\lambda_n} \right]. \qquad (2.56)$$

An expression of identical appearance can be derived from the exponent of the joint probability density of category G. The differences between the two exponents are in the directions of their eigenvectors and the numerical magnitudes of their eigenvalues and ensemble means. Denoting the exponents in the two probability densities by $f(\mathbf{v})$ and $g(\mathbf{v})$, we can write the logarithm of the likelihood ratio as in Eq. (2.57), where K is a constant that involves the ratio of determinants of the two covariance matrices.

$$\log l(\mathbf{v}) = K + f(\mathbf{v}) - g(\mathbf{v}), \qquad \text{where } K = \log\left(|\mathbf{U}_G|^{1/2}/|\mathbf{U}_F|^{1/2}\right). \quad (2.57)$$

Now we shall show that $S(\mathbf{v}, \{\mathbf{f}_m\}) = \text{constant}$ [see Eq. (2.20)] satisfies Eq. (2.55), and that the decision, comparison of the two sides of Eq. (2.42), is identical with basing decisions on the likelihood ratio by means of comparing Eq. (2.57) with a constant. It will be recalled that S is the mean-square Euclidean distance between $\mathbf{v}$ and members of $\{\mathbf{f}_m\}$ after both are transformed by a linear transformation that consists of a rotation $\mathbf{C}$ and a diagonal transformation $\mathbf{W}$. The rotation $\mathbf{C}$ is identical with that defined above, and the elements of the diagonal transformation are the reciprocal standard deviations of $\{\mathbf{f}_m\}$ in the directions of the eigenvectors. The mean-square distance S may therefore be expressed by Eq. (2.58). With the use of Eq. (2.50b) this can be simplified to Eq. (2.59), where $\mathbf{Y}_m$ is the transformation of $\mathbf{f}_m$.

$$S(\mathbf{v}, \{\mathbf{f}_m\}) = \overline{(\mathbf{v} - \mathbf{f}_m)\,\mathbf{CWIW}^T\mathbf{C}^T\,(\mathbf{v} - \mathbf{f}_m)^T}^{\,m} = \text{constant} \qquad (2.58)$$

$$= \overline{(\mathbf{y} - \mathbf{Y}_m)\,\mathbf{WIW}^T\,(\mathbf{y} - \mathbf{Y}_m)^T}^{\,m}. \qquad (2.59)$$

But $\mathbf{WIW}^T$ is a diagonal matrix with elements equal to the reciprocal variances of $\{\mathbf{f}_m\}$. From a comparison of Eqs. (2.24c) and (2.40) we see that the variances are equal to the eigenvalues; and we obtain Eq. (2.60). Substituting this in Eq. (2.59) yields Eq. (2.61).

$$\mathbf{WIW}^T = \Lambda^{-1}. \qquad (2.60)$$

$$\text{Constant} = \overline{(\mathbf{y} - \mathbf{Y}_m)\,\Lambda^{-1}\,(\mathbf{y} - \mathbf{Y}_m)^T}^{\,m}. \qquad (2.61)$$

Eq. (2.61) can be brought into the form of the exponent of the joint probability density, Eq. (2.56). Writing Eq. (2.61) as a sum and bringing averaging under the summation sign yields

$$\text{constant} = \sum_{n=1}^{N} \overline{\frac{(y_n - Y_{mn})^2}{\lambda_n}}^{\,m} = \sum_{n=1}^{N} \left[\overline{\frac{(y_n - Y_{mn})^2}{\lambda_n}}^{\,m}\right] \qquad (2.62)$$

Expanding the square and adding and subtracting $\overline{Y_n}^{\,2}$ from each term of the numerator results in Eq. (2.63).

$$\text{Constant} = \sum_{n=1}^{N} \frac{y_n^{\,2} - 2y_n\overline{Y_n} + \overline{Y_n^{\,2}}}{\lambda_n} =$$

$$= \sum_{n=1}^{N} \frac{y_n^{\,2} - 2y_n\overline{Y_n} + \overline{Y_n}^{\,2} + \overline{Y_n^{\,2}} - \overline{Y_n}^{\,2}}{\lambda_n}. \qquad (2.63)$$

Since $\overline{Y_n} = m_n$, and $\overline{Y_n^2} - \overline{Y_n}^2 = \sigma_n^2 = \lambda_n$, this equation can be written in the simplified form of Eq. (2.64), which is recognized as containing the exponent $f(\mathbf{v})$ of the joint probability density.

$$\text{Constant} = \sum_{n=1}^{N} \frac{(y_n - m_n)^2 + \lambda_n}{\lambda_n} =$$

$$= N + \sum_{n=1}^{N} \frac{(y_n - m_n)^2}{\lambda_n} = N + f(\mathbf{v}). \qquad (2.64)$$

The difference of the two measures—the mean-square distance of $\mathbf{v}$ to category F minus its mean-square distance to category G—is given in Eq. (2.65) and is seen to be a measure of the logarithm of the likelihood ratio expressed in Eq. (2.57).*

$$\text{Threshold } T \gtrless S_F(\mathbf{v}, \{\mathbf{f}_m\}) - S_G(\mathbf{v}, \{\mathbf{g}_m\}). \qquad (2.65a)$$

$$T \gtrless f(\mathbf{v}) - g(\mathbf{v}). \qquad (2.65b)$$

Thus fitting Gaussian probability densities to the sets of labeled samples of the classes is equivalent to the measurement of Euclidean distances to the means of classes after linear transformations of the vector space. In effect the best fitting ellipsoidal region is fitted to the set of samples, and closeness to the center is measured in ellipsoidal units of equidistant contours.

In the special case where the transformation is diagonal (feature weighting), the axes of the ellipsoids must be parallel to the original set of coordinate directions. The limitations of these methods are evident from the geometrical interpretation given. A more detailed explanation of limitations will be given in Chapter V.

2.8 CLASSIFICATION BY SEPARATION OF CLASSES

The central concept described in the preceding sections is that non-identical events of a category may be considered close by some method of measuring distance. This measure of distance is placed in evidence by that transformation of the signal space that brings together like events

---

*Slight differences between likelihood ratio computation and mean-square distance computation arise from the choice of the constraint's numerical value in the minimization problems stated earlier. This affects the scale factor associated with S.

by clustering them most. No specific attempt was made, however, to ensure that the transformations developed should separate events of different categories.

We shall now introduce criteria for developing optimum transformations that not only cluster events of the same class but also separate those that belong to different classes. Consider, for example, the transformation that maximizes the mean-square distance between points that belong to different classes while it minimizes the mean-square distance between points of the same class. The effect of such a transformation is illustrated in Fig. 2–7, where like events have been clustered through minimization of intraset distances, and clusters have been separated from each other through the maximization of interset distances. The

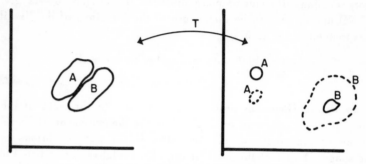

Figure 2-7. Separation of classes.

transformation that accomplishes the stated objectives can be specified by the following problems.

Problem 1

Find the transformation T within a specified class of transformations that maximizes the mean-square interset distance, after transformation, subject to the constraint that the sum of the mean-square interset and intraset distances is held constant.

Note that for the sake of simplifying the mathematics, the minimization of intraset distances was converted to a constraint on the maximization problem. If interset distances are maximized, and the sum of interset and intraset distances is constant, then it follows that intraset distances are minimized. We may impose the additional constraint that the mean-square intraset distance of each class shall be equal, after transformation, thereby avoiding the possible preferential treatment of one class over another. Without the latter constraint the situation indicated with dotted lines in Fig. 2-7 may occur where minimization of the sum of intraset distances may leave one set more clustered than the other.

This criterion of optimization is given as an illustrative example of how one may convert the desirable objective of separation of classes to a mathematically expressible and solvable problem. Several alternate ways of stating the desired objectives as well as choosing the constraints are possible. For example, the mean-square intraset distance could be minimized while holding the interset distances constant. Another alternative is to minimize intraset distances while holding the distances between the means a constant. It can be shown that the solution of this minimization problem results in a transformation which, together with the decision rule postulated to differentiate between members of the different classes, has a counterpart in decision theory.

Techniques that discriminate between members of different classes by use of a single function of the space will be referred to as discriminant techniques. The above statements of the problem, when the transformations are linear, are known as linear discriminants.

Problem 2

A second, even more interesting criterion for optimum categorization is the optimization of the classificatory decision on the labeled events. Classificatory decisions, in the preceding were ultimately based on comparing the similarity S (mean-square distance) of the event $\mathbf{p}$ with the known events of each class. If $\mathbf{p}$ is chosen as any member of class A, for example, we would like to have $S|\mathbf{p}, \{\mathbf{a}_m\}| < S|\mathbf{p}, \{\mathbf{b}_m\}|$, on the average, where $\{\mathbf{b}_m\}$ is the set of known members of any other class B. Similarly, if $\mathbf{p}$ is any member of B, then $S|\mathbf{p}, \{\mathbf{b}_m\}| < S|\mathbf{p}, \{\mathbf{a}_m\}|$. The two desirable requirements are conveniently combined in the statement of the following problem.

Find the transformation of a given class of transformations that maximizes $S|\mathbf{p}, \{\mathbf{b}_m\}| - S|\mathbf{p}, \{\mathbf{a}_m\}|$, on the average, if $\mathbf{p}$ belongs to category A, while requiring that the average of $S|\mathbf{p}, \{\mathbf{a}_m\}| - S|\mathbf{p}, \{\mathbf{b}_m\}|$ for any $\mathbf{p}$ contained in category B be a positive constant. The constraint of this problem assures that not only points of category A, but also those of B are classified correctly, on the average. The symmetrical situation where $S|\mathbf{p}, \{\mathbf{a}_m\}| - S|\mathbf{p}, \{\mathbf{b}_m\}|$ for $\mathbf{p} \, \epsilon \, B$ is also maximized leads to the same solution.

It is important to note that the above problem is not aimed at maximizing the number of correct decisions. Instead it makes the correct decisions most unequivocal, on the average. It is substantially more difficult to maximize the number of correct classifications. That will be treated in Section 3.7.

2.9 A CLASS-SEPARATING TRANSFORMATION

The particular linear transformation that maximizes the mean-square interset distance while holding the sum of the mean-square interset and intraset distances constant is developed below. Recall that the purpose of this transformation is to separate events of dissimilar categories while clustering those that belong to the same class.

The mean-square distance between the M_1 members of the set $\{f_m\}$ and the M_2 members of the set $\{g_p\}$, after their linear transformation, is given in Eq. (2.66), where f_{ms} and g_{ps} are, respectively, the sth components of the mth and p^{th} members of the sets $\{f_m\}$ and $\{g_p\}$. For the sake of notational simplicity this mean-square interset distance is denoted by $S[\{f_m\}, \{g_p\}]$ and is the quantity to be maximized by a suitable choice of the linear transformation. The choice of the notation above is intended to signify that the transformation to be found is a function of the two sets.

$$S(\{f_m\}, \{g_p\}) = \frac{1}{M_1 M_2} \sum_{m=1}^{M_1} \sum_{p=1}^{M_2} \sum_{n=1}^{N} \left[\sum_{s=1}^{N} w_{ns}(f_{ms} - g_{ps}) \right]^2. \qquad (2.66)$$

The constraint that the mean-square distance θ between points, regardless of the set to which they belong, is a constant, is expressed by Eq. (2.67), where γ is the coefficient of any point belonging to the union of the sets $\{f_m\}$ and $\{g_p\}$, $M_T = \binom{M_1 + M_2}{2}$, and $M = M_1 + M_2$.

$$\theta = \frac{1}{M_T} \sum_{m=1}^{M} \sum_{p=1}^{M} \sum_{n=1}^{N} \left[\sum_{s=1}^{N} w_{ns}(\gamma_{ms} - \gamma_{ps}) \right]^2 = \text{constant } K. \qquad (2.67)$$

Both of the above equations may be simplified by expanding the squares as double sums and interchanging the order of summations. Carrying out the indicated operations, we obtain Eqs. (2.68) and (2.69).

$$S\{f_m\}, \{g_p\}) = \sum_{n=1}^{N} \sum_{s=1}^{N} \sum_{r=1}^{N} w_{ns} w_{nr} x_{sr}, \qquad (2.68a)$$

where

$$x_{sr} = x_{rs} = \frac{1}{M_1 M_2} \sum_{m=1}^{M_1} \sum_{p=1}^{M_2} (f_{ms} - g_{ps})(f_{mr} - g_{pr}) \qquad (2.68b)$$

and

$$\theta = \sum_{n=1}^{N} \sum_{s=1}^{N} \sum_{r=1}^{N} w_{ns} w_{nr} t_{sr} = K, \qquad (2.69a)$$

where

$$t_{sr} = t_{rs} = \frac{1}{M_T} \sum_{m=1}^{M} \sum_{p=1}^{M} (y_{ms} - y_{ps})(y_{mr} - y_{pr}). \qquad (2.69b)$$

The coefficient x_{sr} is the general element of the matrix **X** which is of the form of a covariance matrix and arises from considerations of cross-set distances. The matrix **T** with general coefficient t_{sr}, on the other hand, arises from considerations involving distances between the total number of points of all sets.

We now maximize Eq. (2.68), subject to the constraint of Eq. (2.69a), by the method of Lagrange multipliers. Since dw_{ns} is arbitrary in Eq. (2.70), Eq. (2.71) must be satisfied.

$$dS - \lambda d\theta = \sum_{n=1}^{N} \sum_{s=1}^{N} dw_{ns} \left[\sum_{r=1}^{N} w_{nr}(x_{sr} - \lambda t_{sr}) \right] = 0. \qquad (2.70)$$

$$\therefore \sum_{r=1}^{N} w_{nr}(x_{sr} - \lambda t_{sr}) = 0 \qquad n = 1, 2, \ldots, N; \qquad s = 1, 2, \ldots, N. \qquad (2.71)$$

Equation (2.71) can be written in matrix notation to exhibit the solution in an illuminating way. If we let $\mathbf{w}_n$ be a vector with N components, $w_{n1} \ldots w_{nN}$, then Eq. (2.71) may be written as

$$\mathbf{w}_1(\mathbf{X} - \lambda \mathbf{T}) = 0$$
$$\cdots\cdots\cdots\cdots$$
$$\mathbf{w}_n(\mathbf{X} - \lambda \mathbf{T}) = 0 \qquad\qquad (2.72a)$$
$$\cdots\cdots\cdots\cdots$$
$$\mathbf{w}_N(\mathbf{X} - \lambda \mathbf{T}) = 0.$$

By postmultiplying both sides of the equation by T^{-1}, we obtain Eq. (2.72b), which is in the form of an eigenvalue problem.

$$\mathbf{w}_1(\mathbf{XT}^{-1} - \lambda \mathbf{I}) = 0$$
$$\mathbf{w}_2(\mathbf{XT}^{-1} - \lambda \mathbf{I}) = 0 \qquad\qquad (2.72b)$$
$$\cdots\cdots\cdots\cdots\cdots$$
$$\mathbf{w}_N(\mathbf{XT}^{-1} - \lambda \mathbf{I}) = 0.$$

T is positive definite. Equations (2.72a) and (2.72b) can be satisfied in either of two ways. Either $\mathbf{w}_n$, the nth row of the linear transformation described by the matrix **W**, is identically zero, or it is an eigenvector of the matrix $\mathbf{XT}^{-1}$. We must make a substitution in the mean-square inter-set distance given by Eq. (2.68a) in order to find the solution that maximizes S. To facilitate this substitution, we recognize that through matrix notation, Eqs. (2.68a) and (2.69a) can be written as Eqs. (2.73) and (2.74).

$$S(\{f_m\}, \{g_p\}) = \sum_{n=1}^{N} \mathbf{w}_n \, \mathbf{X} \mathbf{w}_n{}^{T}. \tag{2.73}$$

$$\theta = \sum_{n=1}^{N} \mathbf{w}_n \, \mathbf{T} \mathbf{w}_n{}^{T} = K. \tag{2.74}$$

But from Eq. (2.72a) we see that $\mathbf{w}_n \, \mathbf{X}$ may always be replaced by $\lambda \mathbf{w}_n \, \mathbf{T}$. Carrying out this substitution in Eq. (2.73), we obtain Eq. (2.75), where the constraint of Eq. (2.74) is also utilized.

$$S(\{f_m\}, \{g_p\}) = \lambda \sum_{n=1}^{N} \mathbf{w}_n \mathbf{T} \mathbf{w}_n{}^{T} = \lambda K. \tag{2.75}$$

It is now apparent that the largest eigenvalue of $(\mathbf{X} - \lambda \mathbf{T}) = 0$ yields the rows of the transformation that maximizes the mean-square interset distance, subject to the constraint that the mean-square value of all distances is a constant. The transformation is stated by Eq. (2.76), where $\mathbf{w}_1 = w_{11}, w_{12}, \ldots, w_{1N} =$ the eigenvector corresponding to $\lambda_{\max}$.

$$\mathbf{W} = \begin{bmatrix} w_{11} & w_{12} \cdots w_{1N} \\ w_{11} & w_{12} \cdots w_{1N} \\ & \cdots \\ w_{11} & w_{12} \cdots w_{1N} \end{bmatrix}. \tag{2.76}$$

The transformation of this equation is singular, which expresses the fact that the projection of the points along the line of maximum mean-square interset distance and minimum intraset distance is the only important feature of events determining their class membership. This is illustrated in Fig. 2-8, where the line aa' is in the direction of the first eigenvector of the matrix $\mathbf{X}\mathbf{T}^{-1}$. A point of unknown classification is

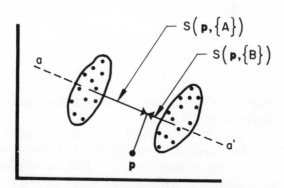

Figure 2-8. Singular class-separating transformation.

grouped in category B because the mean-square difference between its projection on line aa' and the projection of points belonging to set B, $S|\mathbf{p}, \{B\}|$, is less than $S|\mathbf{p}, \{A\}|$, the corresponding difference with members of set A.

Before leaving the discussion of class-separating transformations, a few important facts must be pointed out. A simple formal replacement of the matrices $\mathbf{X}$ and $\mathbf{T}$ with other suitably chosen matrices yields the solution of many interesting and useful problems. It is not the purpose of the following remarks to catalog the problems solved by the formal solution previously obtained; yet some deserve mention because of their importance. It may be readily verified, for instance, that replacing $\mathbf{T}$ by $\mathbf{I}$ is equivalent to maximizing the between-set distances, subject to the condition that the volume of the space is a constant.

Another replacement that must be singled out is the substitution of the matrix $\mathbf{L}$ for $\mathbf{T}$, where $\mathbf{L}$ is the covariance matrix associated with all intraset distances (distances among like events). Eigenvectors of $(\mathbf{X} - \lambda\mathbf{L})$ form rows of the transformation that maximizes interset distances while holding intraset distances constant. This problem is essentially the same as the maximization of interset distances while holding the sum of interset and intraset distances constant, yet the relative separation of sets achieved by the two transformations is different. The difference may be exhibited by computing the ratio of the mean-square separation of sets to the mean clustering of elements within the same set, as measured by the mean-square intraset distance. It can be concluded, therefore, that the constraint employed in the maximization of interset distances does have an influence on the degree of separation achieved between sets.

Throughout this section the class-separating transformations were developed by reference to the existence of only two sets, $\{\mathbf{f}_m\}$ and $\{\mathbf{g}_p\}$. The results obtained by these methods are more general, however, because they apply directly to the separation of an arbitrary number of sets. For instance, in the maximization of the mean-square interset distance, there is no reason why the matrix $\mathbf{X}$ should involve interset distances between only two sets. An arbitrary number of sets may be involved, and the interset distances are simply all those distances measured between two points not in the same set. Similar arguments are valid for all the other matrices involved. The only precaution that must be taken concerns the possible use of additional constraints specifying preferential or nonpreferential treatment of classes. These additional constraints may require, for instance, that the mean-square intraset distance of all sets be equal or be related to each other by constants. Aside from these minor matters, the results apply to the separation of any number of classes.

2.10 MAXIMIZATION OF CORRECT CLASSIFICATIONS

The correct classification of points of the set F are made more unequivocal by the linear transformation that brings any event f_n of set F closer to members of F, on the average, than to those of another set G. One of the ways in which the average unequivocalness of correct classificatory decisions may be stated mathematically is to require that a numerical value associated with the quality of a decision be maximized, on the average. Of the several quantitative measures of the quality of a decision that may be defined, one that readily lends itself to mathematical treatment is given in Eq. (2.77). The difference in the values of the function S evaluated for the point $\mathbf{p}$ and each of the two sets, F and G, is a quantity Q, which increases as the decision regarding the classification of $\mathbf{p}$ becomes more unequivocal.

$$S(\mathbf{p}, \{\mathbf{g}_m\}) - S(\mathbf{p}, \{\mathbf{f}_m\}) = Q. \tag{2.77}$$

Since decisions in previous sections were based on the comparison of Q with a suitable threshold value (such as zero), we now want to find that linear transformation that maximizes Q, on the average, whenever Q is to be positive. If $\mathbf{p}$ is a member of the set F, then $\mathbf{p}$ is closer to F than to G, and thus Q is to be positive. The maximization of Q for $\mathbf{p} \, \epsilon \, F$ results in maximizing the margin with which correct decisions are made, on the average. The foregoing maximization is stated in Eq. (2.78), subject to the constraint expressed by Eq. (2.79). The latter simply states that if $\mathbf{p} \, \epsilon \, G$, the average decision is still correct, as measured by the margin K.

$$\overline{S(\mathbf{f}_n, \{\mathbf{g}_p\}) - S(\mathbf{f}_n, \{\mathbf{f}_m\})}^n = \overline{Q} = \text{maximum}, \tag{2.78}$$

subject to

$$\overline{S(\mathbf{g}_n, \{\mathbf{f}_m\}) - S(\mathbf{g}_n, \{\mathbf{g}_p\})}^n = \overline{K} + \text{constant} > 0. \tag{2.79}$$

Maximization of $\overline{Q} + \overline{K}$ has the same solution.

By utilizing previously obtained results, these equations are readily solved for the optimum linear transformation. Rewriting the first term of Eq. (2.78), we note that it expresses the mean-square interset distance between sets F and G and may be written as in Eq. (2.80), where Eq. (2.78) and the simplifying notation of Eq. (2.68) are employed.

$$\overline{S(\mathbf{f}_n, \{\mathbf{g}_p\})}^n = S(\{\mathbf{f}_n\}, \{\mathbf{g}_p\}) =$$

$$= \frac{1}{M_1 M_2} \sum_{m=1}^{M_1} \sum_{p=1}^{M_2} \sum_{n=1}^{N} \left[\sum_{s=1}^{N} w_{ns}(f_{ms} - g_{ps}) \right]^2. \tag{2.80a}$$

$$\overline{S(\mathbf{f}_n, \{\mathbf{g}_p\})}^n = \sum_{n=1}^{N} \sum_{s=1}^{N} \sum_{r=1}^{N} w_{ns} w_{nr} x_{sr}. \qquad (2.80\text{b})$$

The second term of Eq. (2.78) is the mean-square intraset distance of set F and can be expressed as in Eq. (2.81). The argument of the covariance coefficient $u_{sr}(F)$ signifies that it is a covariance of elements of the set F.

$$\overline{S(\mathbf{f}_n, \{\mathbf{f}_m\})}^n = S(\{\mathbf{f}_n\}, \{\mathbf{f}_m\}) =$$

$$= \frac{1}{(M_1 - 1) M_1} \sum_{p=1}^{M_1} \sum_{m=1}^{M_1} \sum_{n=1}^{N} \left[\sum_{s=1}^{N} w_{ns} (f_{ps} - f_{ms}) \right]^2. \qquad (2.81\text{a})$$

$$\overline{S(\mathbf{f}_n, \{\mathbf{f}_m\})}^n = \frac{2M_1}{M_1 - 1} \sum_{n=1}^{N} \sum_{s=1}^{N} \sum_{r=1}^{N} w_{ns} w_{nr} u_{sr}(F). \qquad (2.81\text{b})$$

Similarly, the first term of Eq. (2.79) is the mean-square interset distance, and the second term is the intraset distance of set G. The maximization problem can thus be restated by Eqs. (2.82a) and (2.82b).

$$\text{Maximize } \overline{Q} = \sum_{n=1}^{N} \sum_{s=1}^{N} \sum_{r=1}^{N} w_{ns} w_{nr} \left[x_{sr} - \frac{2M_1}{M_1 - 1} u_{sr}(F) \right], \qquad (2.82\text{a})$$

subject to

$$\overline{K} = \sum_{n=1}^{N} \sum_{s=1}^{N} \sum_{r=1}^{N} w_{ns} w_{nr} \left[x_{sr} - \frac{2M_2}{M_2 - 1} u_{sr}(G) \right]. \qquad (2.82\text{b})$$

Following the methods used earlier, we can write the solution of this problem by inspection.

$$d\overline{Q} - \lambda d\overline{K} = \sum_{n=1}^{N} \sum_{s=1}^{N} dw_{ns} \left[\sum_{r=1}^{N} w_{nr} \left\{ x_{sr} - \right. \right.$$

$$\left. \left. - \frac{2M_1}{M_1 - 1} u_{sr}(F) - \lambda \left(x_{sr} - \frac{2M_2}{M_2 - 1} u_{sr}(G) \right) \right\} \right]. \qquad (2.83)$$

From Eq. (2.83) it follows that Eq. (2.84a) must hold, where a_{sr} and β_{sr} are given by Eqs. (2.84b) and (2.84c).

$$\sum_{r=1}^{N} w_{nr} (a_{sr} - \lambda \beta_{sr}) = 0 \qquad n = 1, 2, \dots, N; \qquad s = 1, 2, \dots, N. \qquad (2.84\text{a})$$

$$a_{sr} = x_{sr} - \frac{2M_1}{M_1 - 1} u_{sr}(F). \qquad (2.84\text{b})$$

$$\beta_{sr} = x_{sr} - \frac{2M_2}{M_2 - 1}\, u_{sr}(G).\qquad (2.84c)$$

By reference to earlier results, such as those expressed by Eq. (2.71), the transformation whose coefficients w_{ns} satisfy an equation of the preceding form is the solution of the eigenvalue problem of Eq. (2.85), where $\mathbf{w}_n$ is a row of the matrix expressing the linear transformation

$$\begin{aligned}
\mathbf{w}_1(a - \lambda\beta) &= 0\\
\mathbf{w}_2(a - \lambda\beta) &= 0\\
&\;\cdots\cdots\cdots\cdots\\
\mathbf{w}_N(a - \lambda\beta) &= 0.
\end{aligned}\qquad (2.85)$$

Analogous to the arguments used in the previous section, the above solution yields a singular transformation. Forcing the transformation to be nonsingular results in the optimum transformation as an orthogonal transformation, where each row of the matrix $\mathbf{W}$ is an eigenvector of $(a - \lambda\beta) = 0$. Furthermore, it is readily shown that the solution so obtained indeed maximizes $\overline{Q}$.

It is interesting to note that the maximization of the average correct classifications can be considered as the maximization of the difference between interset and intraset distances. This alternate statement of the problem can be exhibited by the addition of Eq. (2.82b) to Eq. (2.82a).

$$\overline{Q} + \overline{K} = \sum_{n=1}^{N}\sum_{s=1}^{N}\sum_{r=1}^{N} w_{ns} w_{nr}\left[2x_{sr} - \right.$$

$$\left. -\left\{ \frac{2M_1}{M_1 - 1}\, u_{sr}(F) + \frac{2M_2}{M_2 - 1}\, u_{sr}(G) \right\}\right].\qquad (2.86)$$

But the expression within the braces is simply the covariance l_{sr} associated with all intraset distances. Since K is a constant, the maximization of Eq. (2.86) is equivalent to the maximization of $\overline{Q}$.

In summing up the results of this section, we see that the problem of learning to distinguish between events of different categories, while profiting from knowledge of members of all categories, can be treated as a maximization or minimization problem. A linear transformation is found from a class of transformations that solves mathematical problems that express the desire not only to cluster events known to belong to the same category but also to separate those that belong to different categories. Within the restricted class of transformations considered in this section, the solutions are in the form of eigenvalue problems which emphasize properties that samples of a category have in common, and which at the same time differ from properties of other categories.

2.11 MACHINE LEARNING AND CLASSIFICATION

In the following section two distinct modes of operation of the recognition system will be distinguished. The first consists of the sequential introduction of a set of events, each labeled according to the category to which it belongs. During this period, we want to identify the common pattern of the inputs that allows their classification into their respective categories. As part of the process of learning to categorize, the estimate of what the category is must also be updated to include each new event as it is introduced. The process of updating the estimate of the common pattern consists of recomputing the new measures of similarity so that they include the new, labeled event on which the quantitative measures of similarity are based.

During the second mode of operation the event **p**, which is to be classified, is compared to each of the sets of labeled events by the measure of similarity found best for each set. The event is then classified as a member of that category to which it is most similar.

It is not possible to state with certainty that the pattern has been successfully learned or recognized from a set of its samples because information is not available on how samples were selected to represent the class. Nevertheless, it is possible to obtain a quantitative indication of our certainty of having obtained a correct method of determining membership in the category from the ensemble of similar events. As each new event is introduced, its "distance" to the members of the sets already presented is measured by the function S defined earlier. The magnitude of the number S indicates how close the new event is to those already introduced. As S is refined and, with each new example, improves its ability to recognize the class, the numerical measure of distance between new examples and the class will tend to decrease, on the average. Strictly speaking, of course, this last statement cannot be true, in general. It may be true only if the categories to be distinguished are separable by functions S taken from the class that we have considered; even under this condition the statement is true only if certain assumptions are made regarding the statistical distribution of the samples on which we learn. In cases in which no knowledge regarding the satisfaction of either of these two requirements exists, convergence of the similarity as the sample size is increased is simply wishful thinking, the heuristic justification of which is based on the minimization problem solved in developing S.

Figure 2–9 illustrates the mechanization of the learning and recognition modes of the classificatory process discussed thus far. For the sake of clarity, the elementary block diagram of the process distinguishes only between two categories of events, but it can be readily extended to distinguish between an arbitrary number of categories. It should be noted that one of the categories may be the complement of all others. The admission of such a category into the set is only one of the ways in which a machine that is always forced to classify events into known categories may be made to decide that an event does not belong to any of the desired ones; it belongs to the category of "everything else." Samples of "everything else" must, of course, be given.

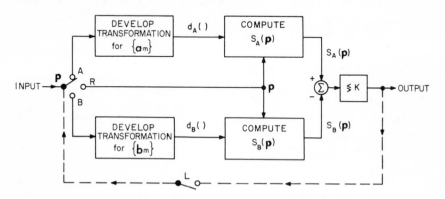

Figure 2-9. Elementary block diagram of the classification process.

During the first mode of operation, the input to the machine is a set of labeled events. Let us follow its behavior through an example. Suppose that a number of events, some belonging to set A and some to set B, have already been introduced. According to the method already described the optimum transformations (one for each class) that minimize the mean-square distance between samples of the same class have been found. As a new labeled event is introduced (say that it belongs to set A), the switch at the input is first turned to the recognition mode R so that the new event $\mathbf{p}$ can be compared to set A as well as to set B through the functions $S_A(\mathbf{p}) = S(\mathbf{p}, \{a_m\})$ and $S_B(\mathbf{p})$, which were computed before the introduction of $\mathbf{p}$. The comparison of S_A and S_B with a threshold K indicates whether the point $\mathbf{p}$ would be classified as belonging to A or to B from knowledge available up to the present. Since the true membership of $\mathbf{p}$ is known (the event is labeled), we can now determine whether $\mathbf{p}$ would be classified correctly or incorrectly. The input switch is then turned to A so that $\mathbf{p}$, which indeed belongs to A, can be included in the computation of the best transformation of set A.

When the next labeled event is introduced (let us say that it belongs to set B), the input switch is again turned to R in order to test the ability of the machine to classify the new event correctly. After the test, the switch is turned to B so that the event can be included among samples of set B and the optimum function S_B can be recomputed. This procedure is repeated for each new event, and a record is kept of the rate at which incorrect classifications would be made on the known events. When the training period is completed, presumably as a result of satisfactory performance on the selection of known events (sufficiently low error rate), the input switch is left in the recognition mode.

"Supervised learning" takes place in the interval of time in which examples of the categories generate ensembles of points from which the defining features of the classes are obtained by methods previously discussed. "Supervision" is provided by an outside source such as a human being who elects to teach the recognition of patterns by examples and who selects the examples on which to learn.

"Unsupervised learning," by contrast, is a method of learning without the aid of such an outside source. It seems clear, at least intuitively, that the unsupervised learning of membership in specific classes cannot succeed unless it is preceded by a period of supervision during which some concepts regarding the characteristics of classes are established. A specified degree of certainty concerning the patterns has been achieved in the form of a sufficiently low rate of misclassification during the supervised learning period. The achievement of the low misclassification rate, in fact, can be used to signify the end of the learning period, after which the system that performs the operations indicated in Fig. 2–9 can be left to its own devices. It is only after this supervised interval of time that the system can be usefully employed to recognize, without outside aid, events as belonging to one or another of the categories.

Throughout the period of learning on examples, each example is included in the proper set of similar events that influence the changes of the measures of similarity. After supervised activity has ceased, events introduced for classification may belong to any of the categories; and no outside source informs the machine of the correct category. The machine itself, operating on each new event, however, can determine, with the already qualitatively specified probability of error, to which class the event should belong. If the new event is included in the set exemplifying this class, the function measuring membership in the category has been altered. Unsupervised learning results from the successive alterations of the transformations, brought about by the inclusion of events into the sets of labeled events according to determinations of class membership rendered by the machine itself. This learning process is instrumented by the dotted line in Fig. 2–9, which, when the learning switch L is closed, allows the machine's decisions to control routing of the input to the various sets.

To facilitate the illustration of some implications of the process described above, consider the case in which recognition of membership in a single class is desired and all labeled events are members of only that class. In this case, classification of events as members or nonmembers of the category degenerates into the comparison of the similarity S with a threshold T. If S is greater than T, the event is a nonmember; if S is less than T, the event is said to be a member of the class. Since the machine decides that all points of the signal space for which S is less than T are members of the class, the class — as far as the machine is concerned — is the collection of points that lie in a given region in the signal space. For the specific function of S of this chapter, this region is an ellipsoid in the N-dimensional space.

Unsupervised learning is illustrated graphically in Fig. 2-10. The two-dimensional ellipse drawn with a solid line signifies the domain D_1 of the signal space in which any point yields $S < T$. This domain was obtained during supervised activity. If a point p_1 is introduced after supervised learning, so that p_1 lies outside D_1, then p_1 is merely re-jected as a nonmember of the class. If point p_2 contained in D_1 is intro-duced, however, it is judged a member of the class and is included in the set of examples used to generate a new function S and a new domain D_2, designated by the dotted line in Fig. 2-10. A third point p_3, which was a nonmember before the introduction of p_2, becomes recognized as a mem-ber of the class after the inclusion of p_2 in the set of similar events.

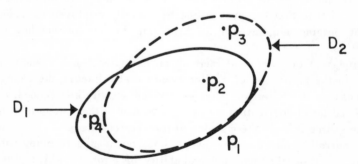

Figure 2-10. Unsupervised learning.

Before leaving the subject of unsupervised learning, which is treated in more detail in Chapter IV, we point out that as the new domain D_2 is formed, points such as p_4 in Fig. 2-10 become excluded from the class. Such an exclusion from the class is analogous to "forgetting" because of lack of repetition. Forgetting is the characteristic of not recognizing p_4 as a member of the class, although at one time it was recognized as belonging to it.

2.12 THRESHOLD SETTING

In the classification of an event $\mathbf{p}$, the mean-square distance between $\mathbf{p}$ and members of each of the categories is computed. The distance between $\mathbf{p}$ and members of a category C is what we called "similarity," $S_C(\mathbf{p})$, where the "sense" in which "distance" is understood depends on the particular category in question. We then stated that, in a manner analogous to decisions based on maximum likelihood ratios, the point $\mathbf{p}$ is classified as a member of the category to which it is most similar. Hence, $\mathbf{p}$ belongs to category C if $S_C(\mathbf{p})$ is less than $S_X(\mathbf{p})$ where X is any of the other categories.

Since in the special case discussed, the function $S_C(\mathbf{p})$, which measures membership in category C, was developed by maximally clustering points of C without separating them from points of other sets, there is no guarantee, in general, that a point of another set B may not be closer to C than to B. This is guaranteed only if points of the sets occupy disjointed regions. A graphical illustration that clarifies the comparison of similarities of a point to the different categories is shown in Fig. 2–11. In this figure the elliptical contours $S_{A_1}(\mathbf{p})$, $S_{A_2}(\mathbf{p})$, ..., indicate the locus of points $\mathbf{p}$ in the signal space at a mean-square distance of 1, 2, ..., from members of category A. The loci of these points are concentric ellipsoids in the N-dimensional signal space, shown here in only two dimensions. Similarly, $S_{B_1}(\mathbf{p})$, $S_{B_2}(\mathbf{p})$, ..., and $S_{C_1}(\mathbf{p})$, $S_{C_2}(\mathbf{p})$, ..., are the loci of those points whose mean-square distance from categories B and C, respectively, are 1, 2, ... Note carefully that the sense in which distance is measured at each of the categories differs as is indicated by the different orientations and eccentricities of the ellipses. The heavy line shows the locus of points at equal mean-square distances from two or more sets according to the manner in which distance is measured to each set. This line, therefore, defines the boundary of each of the categories.

At this point in the discussion it would be helpful to digress from the subject of thresholds and dispel some misconceptions that Fig. 2–11 might create regarding the general nature of the categories found by the method described. Recall that one of the possible ways in which a point not belonging to either category could be so classified was by establishing a separate category for "everything else" and assigning the point to the category to which its mean-square distance is smallest. Another, perhaps more practical, method is to call a point a member of neither category if its mean-square distance to the set of points of any class exceeds some threshold value. If this threshold value is set, for example, at a mean-square distance of 3 for all of the categories in Fig. 2–11,

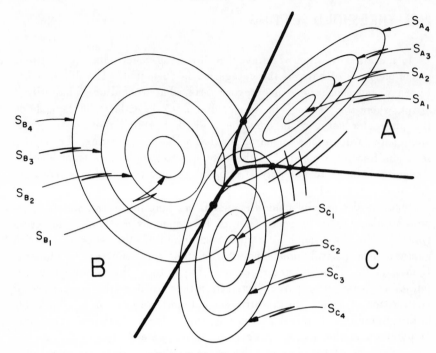

Figure 2-11. Categorization.

then points belonging to A, B, and C will lie inside the three ellipses shown in Fig. 2–12.

It is readily seen, of course, that there is no particular reason why one given minimum mean-square distance should be selected instead of

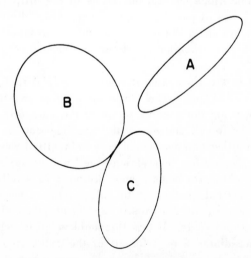

Figure 2-12. Categorization with threshold.

another, or, for that matter, why this minimum distance should be the same for all categories. Many logical and useful criteria may be selected for determining the optimum threshold setting. Here, only one criterion will be singled out as particularly useful. This criterion requires that the minimum thresholds be set so that most of the labeled points fall into the correct category. This is a fundamental criterion, for it requires the system to work best by making the largest number of correct decisions. In decision theory the threshold value depends on the a priori probabilities of the categories and on the costs of false alarm and false dismissal.

The criterion of selecting a threshold that makes the most correct classifications can be applied to our earlier discussions in which the boundary between categories was determined by equating the similarities of a point to two or more categories. In the particular example of Fig. 2–9, where a point could be a member of only one of two categories A and B, the difference $S_A - S_B = 0$ formed the dividing line. There is nothing magical about the threshold zero; we might require that the dividing line between the two categories be $S_A - S_B = K$, where K is a constant chosen from other considerations. A similar problem in communication theory is the choice of a signal-to-noise ratio that serves as the dividing line between calling the received waveform "signal" or calling it "noise." It is understood, of course, that signal-to-noise ratio is an appropriate criterion on which to base decisions (at least in some cases), but the particular value of the ratio to be used as a threshold level must be determined from additional requirements. In communication theory these are usually requirements on the false-alarm or false-dismissal rates. In the problem of choosing the constant K, we may require that it be selected so that most of the labeled points lie in the correct category.

CHAPTER 3

Nonlinear Methods in Classificatory Analysis

In this chapter we will further exploit the fundamental concepts of classificatory analysis through the application of nonlinear techniques. First, we consider the enlargement of the class of transformations so that the distribution of similar events may be altered in a larger variety of ways. Next, we present another geometric interpretation of learning and classification and develop from it a generalized discriminant analysis that results in decision making with a minimum probability of error. An illustrative example is also given. In addition to the methods followed in optimum decision making, two practical problems will be considered. In one we consider the problem of decision making when not all observables are available; some may be missing due to malfunctioning equipment or other reasons. In the other, we consider learning and decision making in a noisy environment. In the concluding section of this chapter we discuss a technique that is specifically intended to be used in cases where only a finite and relatively small number of samples are available. A discriminant function is developed that minimizes the *number* of decision errors.

3.1 ENLARGING THE CLASS OF TRANSFORMATIONS

The central concept motivating the development of techniques presented herein is that there is a transformation that exhibits the class defining common attributes of members of a class, and that this transformation can be found from the solution of a problem that optimizes some property of a set of known events. In the previous chapter, several different properties of the set of known events were investigated in regard to their application as optimization criteria. Clustering of points of the same set, maximal separation of events of different sets, and maximization of the unequivocalness of a classificatory decision were only a few of the criteria investigated. The principal limitation of the results obtained from these considerations stems not from the optimization criteria but from the limitations on the class of transformations or class of random processes among which the optimum was sought.

Achieving success with the linear methods explored thus far requires that the distribution of like events be well fitted inside an ellipsoidal boundary, or, at least, that ellipsoidal boundaries fitted to different categories should not intersect. In discriminant techniques, the different populations of vectors should be separable by hyperplanes. The methods developed in previous sections describe the linear transformation (or the error criterion with which distance is measured), which maximizes the correlation between like events and minimizes it between unlike ones. It is clear, however, that for many categories high correlation may not exist between like events even after their linear transformation. Successful classification even of categories of this type may be achieved, if the class of transformations among which the optimum is sought is enlarged. We recall that use of the class of metrics given in Eq. (3.1) could be viewed as the application of the mean-square error criterion after a linear transformation of the space. With use of the notation often employed in engineering, the metric of Eq. (3.1) can be written as in Eq. (3.2) and can be instrumented by the system of Fig. 3-1.

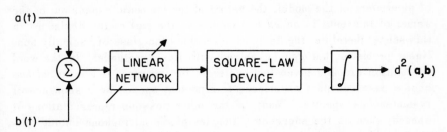

Figure 3-1. Instrumentation of a class of metrics.

$$d^2(\mathbf{a},\ \mathbf{b}) = \sum_{n=1}^{N} \left[\sum_{s=1}^{N} w_{ns}(a_s - b_s) \right]^2 . \qquad (3.1)$$

In Eq. (3.2), $W(t,\ \tau)$ is a linear function of two variables, and the methods previously described simply find the best one that minimizes the output, on the average, or the best one that performs some similar but preselected desirable operation.

$$d^2(\mathbf{a},\ \mathbf{b}) = \int \left[\int W(t, \tau) [a(t) - b(t)] \, dt \right]^2 d\tau. \qquad (3.2)$$

There are many categories of inputs whose members cannot be made "close" by any linear network. Suppose, for instance, that **a** and **b** belong to the category of waveforms that have 5 zero crossings. Since the member waveforms of this category are close to each other in the sense of having the same number of zero crossings and since counting zero crossings is not a linear operation, it is evident that the methods described will fail to learn the correct recognition of membership in the category of interest. On the other hand, it may be quite possible to employ linear methods to solve the problem successfully if inputs are represented by a different set of parameters; that is, if the model of the physical world from which the waveforms were obtained is altered. In this example the waveform acts as its own model. In an arithmetized form, on the other hand, the waveform can be represented by the coefficients of its expansion in one of several suitable generalized harmonic functions. It can also be represented by the results of certain tests that can be performed on the waveform. Linear methods can be forced to solve problems of the type described, if the selection of the model of the physical world includes tests on which a linear function can be found such that, as measured by the function, tests on different members of a category have similar outcomes. An extreme example of such a test is the examination of the waveform in order to establish the number of times its magnitude is less than ϵ. In the example above, waveforms with 5 zero crossings would yield very similar results when subjected to this test, and no function at all is necessary to exhibit this property. The choice of parameters of the model, the nature of the harmonic expansion, or the nature of the tests is an *ad hoc* choice on the part of the designer. In this sense, therefore, the designer determines the class of basically nonlinear problems that can be solved with linear methods. In the word recognition example given in Chapter V, for instance, it was an *ad hoc* choice based on past experience to represent speech by a sequence of instantaneous spectra. Many of the other possible representations of speech, such as the successive samples of the microphone output voltage, could have resulted in the failure of linear methods to learn the categories.

The degree of success achieved by linear methods depends on the choice of the model and the nature of the classes to be recognized. The dependence of success on the choice of the model may be reduced by enlarging the class of transformations within which we search for the optimum one. In the categorization of waveforms of 5 zero crossings, for instance, the correct category definition may be obtained if we do not restrict ourselves to the use of linear networks in Fig. 3-1. If the network contains nonlinear elements, such as flip-flops and the like, it is at least plausible that "having equal numbers of zero crossings" is a category that can be learned.

In the following we would like to consider a class of nonlinear transformations. Whereas before we considered the class obtained by measuring the Euclidean distance after a linear transformation of the vector space, we now consider Euclidean distance measured after a continuous nonlinear transformation of the space. This type of transformation describes the operation of stretching and compressing a rubber sheet to bring members of a set closer to each other.

All the minimization problems of the preceding sections can be extended and carried out for nonlinear transformations as well. In the following section only two of these will be derived as illustrative examples. The first minimization problem is an extension of the method of clustering members of a category after their nonlinear transformation. The second problem is an extension of the method of clustering members of sets while separating sets. This problem is solved—within the class of linear transformations—in Chapter II.

The class of continuous transformations is too general to yield a practical solution. In the discussion that follows, therefore, the class of transformations within which a solution is sought will be restricted to certain polynomial transformations.

Problem 1. A Clustering Transformation

Let us assume that each coordinate of the N-dimensional space undergoes a continuous transformation given by the polynomial of Eq. (3.3), which maps the origin into itself.

$$y_n = \sum_{p=1}^{K} a_{np} v_n^{p}. \qquad (3.3)$$

This transformation is illustrated in Fig. 3–2, which shows that a set of equally spaced grid lines under the transformation can be spaced in an arbitrary manner along each coordinate.

In this way the N-dimensional space can be locally compressed or expanded. The square of the Euclidean distance between two points f_m' and f_s', obtained from the transformation of f_m and f_s, respectively, is expressed by Eq. (3.4).

$$d_e^2(f_m', f_s') = \sum_{n=1}^{N} \left[\sum_{p=1}^{K} a_{np}(f_{mn}^{p} - f_{sn}^{p}) \right]^2. \qquad (3.4)$$

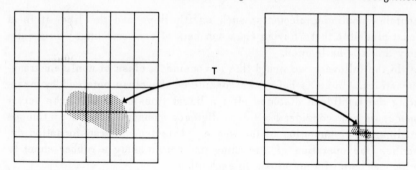

Figure 3-2. A nonlinear transformation.

If coefficients of the polynomial are not restricted, the space may "fold" and a multivalued transformation may result. The Euclidean distance, of course, can be made smaller between two points without the restriction.

The problem is to find the particular nonlinear transformation of the type discussed above which minimizes the mean-square distance between a set of points of a given class after their transformation. In order to obtain a unique solution, we impose the quite arbitrary constraint that a specific point $v_0 = (v_{01}, v_{02}, \ldots, v_{0n})$ should be mapped into another specified point $y_0 = (y_{01}, y_{02}, \ldots, y_{0n})$.

The mean-square distance after transformation is given by Eq. (3.5), where M is the number of elements in the set.

$$S = \overline{d_e^2(f_m', f_s')}^{s,m} = \frac{2M}{(M-1)} \sum_{n=1}^{N} \sum_{p=1}^{K} \sum_{r=1}^{K} a_{np} a_{nr} \left(\overline{f_n^p f_n^r} - \overline{f_n^p} \, \overline{f_n^r} \right). \qquad (3.5)$$

The notation can be simplified by letting Eq. (3.6) express the simplifying substitution that yields Eq. (3.7a). In matrix notation this can be expressed by Eq. (3.7b).

$$\overline{f_n^p f_n^r} - \overline{f_n^p} \, \overline{f_n^r} = u_{pr}(n) = u_{rp}(n). \qquad (3.6)$$

$$\overline{d_e^2(f_m', f_s')}^{s,m} = S(\{f_m'\}, \{f_s'\}) = \frac{2M}{M-1} \sum_{n=1}^{N} \sum_{p=1}^{K} \sum_{r=1}^{K} a_{np} a_{nr} u_{rp}(n) \qquad (3.7a)$$

$$S(\{f_m'\}, \{f_s'\}) = \frac{2M}{M-1} \sum_{n=1}^{N} a_n [U(n)] a_n^T. \qquad (3.7b)$$

The constraint that v_0 map into y_0 is expressed by Eq. (3.8), which contains N constraints, one for each component of the mapping.

$$y_{0n} = \sum_{p=1}^{K} a_{np} v_{0n}^{p} \qquad n = 1, 2, \ldots, N. \tag{3.8}$$

By defining the vector z_n in Eq. (3.9), the above constraint may be readily expressed in vector notation.

$$z_n = (v_{0n}, \ v_{0n}^{2}, \ldots, \ v_{0n}^{p}, \ldots, \ v_{0n}^{k}). \tag{3.9}$$

$$y_{0n} = a_n I z_n^{T} = a_n \cdot z_n \qquad n = 1, 2, \ldots, N. \tag{3.10}$$

By using the method of Lagrange multipliers, S can be minimized subject to the constraints of Eq. (3.10).

$$dS - \sum_{n=1}^{N} \lambda_n \, dy_{0n} = 0. \tag{3.11}$$

In a manner similar to the methods employed earlier, the solution of the minimization problem is expressed by Eq. (3.12), which can be solved for the vector a_n.

$$a_n [U(n)] - \lambda_n z_n = 0 \qquad n = 1, 2, \ldots, N. \tag{3.12a}$$

$$a_n = \lambda_n z_n U^{-1}(n) \qquad n = 1, 2, \ldots, N. \tag{3.12b}$$

The constant λ_n can be evaluated by substituting Eq. (3.12b) into Eq. (3.10) and solving for λ_n.

$$y_{0n} = a_n z_n^{T} = \lambda_n z_n [U^{-1}(n)] \, z_n^{T}; \tag{3.13a}$$

$$\therefore \lambda_n = \frac{y_{0n}}{z_n [U^{-1}(n)] \, z_n^{T}} \tag{3.13b}$$

Substituting the value of λ_n into Eq. (3.12b), we obtain the coefficients of the transformation.

$$a_n = \left(\frac{y_{0n}}{z_n [U^{-1}(n)] z_n^{T}} \right) z_n [U^{-1}(n)]. \tag{3.14}$$

The mean-square distance S can now be computed by substituting Eq. (3.14) in Eq. (3.7b):

$$S_{\min} = \frac{2M}{M-1} \sum_{n=1}^{N} \left(\frac{y_{0n}}{z_n [U^{-1}(n)] \, z_n^{T}} \right)^2 z_n I (z_n [U^{-1}(n)])^{T}, \tag{3.15a}$$

which may be simplified as

$$S_{\min} = \frac{2M}{M-1} \sum_{n=1}^{N} \left(\frac{y_{0n}}{z_n [U^{-1}(n)] \, z_n^{T}} \right)^2 z_n [U^{-1}(n)]^{T} z_n^{T}. \tag{3.15b}$$

Note that $[\mathbf{U}^{-1}(n)]^T = [\mathbf{U}^{-1}(n)]$, since $[\mathbf{U}^{-1}(n)]$ is a symmetric matrix. This fact allows further simplification of $S_{\min}$ and it can be shown that the extremum thus found is indeed a minimum.

$$S_{\min} = \frac{2M}{M-1} \sum_{n=1}^{N} \left(\frac{y_{0n}^2}{\mathbf{z}_n [\mathbf{U}^{-1}(n)] \mathbf{z}_n^T} \right). \tag{3.16}$$

This transformation may be used to further cluster a set of points that have been maximally clustered by linear transformations.

Problem 2. A Class-Separating Transformation

Let us assume that each coordinate of the N-dimensional space undergoes a continuous transformation given by the polynomial of Eq. (3.3). The object of this problem is to find that particular nonlinear transformation that minimizes the mean-square distance between points in the same class, while keeping the distance between the means of the classes constant. Let us assume for simplicity, that there are only two classes, F and G. We see from Eqs. (3.7a) and (3.7b) that the mean-square distance between points in the same class is the quantity Q expressed in Eq. (3.17).

$$\begin{aligned}
Q &= \overline{d_e^2(\mathbf{f}_m', \mathbf{f}_s')}^{s,m} + \overline{d_e^2(\mathbf{g}_m', \mathbf{g}_s')}^{s,m} \\
&= \frac{2M_1}{M_1 - 1} \sum_{n=1}^{N} \mathbf{a}_n [\mathbf{U}_F(n)] \mathbf{a}_n^T + \frac{2M_2}{M_2 - 1} \sum_{n=1}^{N} \mathbf{a}_n [\mathbf{U}_G(n)] \mathbf{a}_n^T,
\end{aligned} \tag{3.17}$$

where M_1 and M_2 are the number of given samples of F and G respectively. The other symbols have the same meanings as in the preceding problem. The simplification of Eq. (3.17) results from the definition of the matrix $[\hat{\mathbf{U}}(n)]$, given in Eq. (3.18b).

$$Q = \sum_{n=1}^{N} \mathbf{a}_n [\hat{\mathbf{U}}(n)] \mathbf{a}_n^T, \tag{3.18a}$$

where

$$[\hat{\mathbf{U}}(n)] = \frac{2M_1}{M_1 - 1} [\mathbf{U}_F(n)] + \frac{2M_2}{M_2 - 1} [\mathbf{U}_G(n)]. \tag{3.18b}$$

The distance between the means of the transformed sets of points is given in Eq. (3.19) and is denoted by the constant K.

$$K = \sum_{n=1}^{N} \left[\sum_{p=1}^{K} a_{np} \left(\overline{f_n^p} - \overline{g_n^p} \right) \right]^2 \tag{3.19}$$

$$K = \sum_{n=1}^{N} \sum_{p=1}^{K} \sum_{q=1}^{K} a_{np} a_{nq} \left(\overline{f_n^p} - \overline{g_n^p} \right) \left(\overline{f_n^q} - \overline{g_n^q} \right) = \sum_{n=1}^{N} \mathbf{a}_n [\mathbf{B}(n)] \, \mathbf{a}_n^T, \quad \left(\begin{array}{c} 3.19 \\ \text{contd.} \end{array} \right)$$

where $[\mathbf{B}(n)]$ is a matrix that has a general element b_{pq} given by

$$b_{pq} = b_{qp} = \left(\overline{f_n^p} - \overline{g_n^p} \right) \left(\overline{f_n^q} - \overline{g_n^q} \right). \tag{3.20}$$

The minimization of Q subject to the constraint K can be carried out by the method of Lagrange multipliers, and results in the familiar solution given in Eq. (3.21).

$$\min (\mathbf{Q} - \lambda \, K) \qquad \mathbf{a}_n [\hat{\mathbf{U}}(n) - \lambda \, \mathbf{B}(n)] = 0. \tag{3.21}$$

The optimum nonlinear transformation that clusters members of the classes while it keeps the classes separated is a polynomial transformation in which the polynomial coefficients are components of the eigenvector corresponding to the smallest eigenvalue of Eq. (3.21).

3.2 GENERALIZED DISCRIMINANT FUNCTIONS

The geometrical interpretation of making decisions of classification is that the vector space in which events are represented by points must be divided into nonintersecting regions, one region corresponding to each of the categories. A classification decision consists of assigning to the event to be classified the name of the category associated with the region in which the event is located.

The decision procedure of the preceding sections constructed the boundaries of these regions and the notion of "inside" versus "outside." The optimum size, shape, and location for the boundaries was derived within the possible shapes that the class of transformations considered at the time was able to generate.

The objective of the following discussion is to present a different geometrical interpretation of making classification decisions that leads to a generalized discriminant analysis. The relationship between the two interpretations will be shown.

In order to recognize membership of a vector in a class represented by a set of sample vectors, we want to find some invariant property of the set of samples. Let the invariant property be $u_1(v_1, v_2, \ldots, v_N)$, some function of the vector $\mathbf{v}$. Invariance is understood to mean that the function $u_1(\mathbf{v})$ will have substantially the same value, say K_1, whenever $\mathbf{v}$ is a member of class F. Similarly, $u_2(\mathbf{v})$ is another function of the vector $\mathbf{v}$ which is such that whenever $\mathbf{v}$ is a member of another class, G, $u_2(\mathbf{v})$ will have substantially the same value, say K_2, but $K_2 \neq K_1$.

Since, according to our original assumptions, any arbitrary point $\mathbf{v}$ can be the member of only one class,* we can assume a function $u(\mathbf{v})$ which is such that whenever $\mathbf{v}$ is contained in class F, $u(\mathbf{v}) \approx K_1$ and whenever $\mathbf{v}$ is contained in class G, $u(\mathbf{v}) \approx K_2$. The function $u(\mathbf{v})$ is a surface over the multidimensional space, and it is so constructed that along the u axis known samples of the different classes fall into disjointed, non-overlapping intervals. Figure 3–3 illustrates this situation for a two-dimensional vector space, where $u(v_1, v_2)$ is a three-dimensional surface. The heights of the surface over samples of class F are highly clustered, and the classes along $u(v_1, v_2)$ are separable. It is readily appreciated that regardless of the manner in which points of the sets F and G are distributed, a surface can always be constructed that clusters members of F and members of G along the height of the surface and keeps the two clusters apart. Furthermore, it does not matter that a class has several disjointed subclasses, as shown in Fig. 3-3. In spoken word recognition, for example, F_1 may represent male utterances and F_2 may represent female utterances of the same word; yet the function $u(\mathbf{v})$ has the same value over both F_1 and F_2.

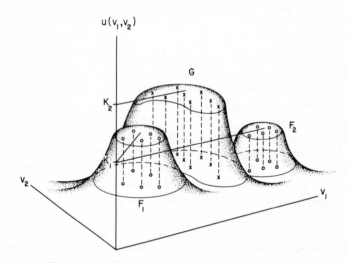

Figure 3-3. Under transformation $u(v_1, v_2)$, F and G are separable.

We shall now show that minimization of the mean-square distance between members of the same class after a transformation of the vector space is equivalent to the process of constructing a surface $u(\mathbf{v})$ in such

---

*The procedure described is equally good if this assumption is not made; i.e., we permit noisy observations of F and G to result in the same vector.

a way that it has minimum variance about the mean over members of the same class.

The mean-square distance after transformation $u(\mathbf{v})$ is given in Eq. (3.22a). Squaring and averaging with respect to m and n yields Eq. (3.22b), where $\sigma_u^2(F)$ stands for the variance after transformation $u(\mathbf{v})$ of the set of points contained in F.

$$d^2(\mathbf{f}_m', \mathbf{f}_n') = \frac{1}{M_2} \sum_{m=1}^{M} \sum_{n=1}^{M} [u(\mathbf{f}_m) - u(\mathbf{f}_n)]^2 \tag{3.22a}$$

$$= \frac{1}{M^2} \sum_{m=1}^{M} \sum_{n=1}^{M} [u^2(\mathbf{f}_m) - 2u(\mathbf{f}_m)u(\mathbf{f}_n) + u^2(\mathbf{f}_n)] \tag{3.22b}$$

$$= 2\overline{u^2(F)} - 2\overline{u(F)}^2 = 2\sigma_u^2(F).$$

The class of functions u within which the minimization is carried out again limits the nature of the distributions of F and G samples that can be successfully classified. In particular, if the function $u(\mathbf{v})$ is of the form given in Eq. (3.23), then, by suitable choice of the degree K, a very general nonlinear function can be approximated arbitrarily closely in a finite region of the vector space.

$$u(v_1, v_2, \ldots, v_N) = \sum_{n=0}^{K} \cdots \sum_{j=0}^{K} \sum_{i=0}^{K} a_{ij \cdots n} v_1^i v_2^j \cdots v_N^n. \tag{3.23}$$

The decision rule of the previous sections can now be given another simple geometrical interpretation. A decision consists of evaluating the height of the surface over the vector to be classified and of comparing this height $u(\mathbf{v})$ with the average heights over the two sets of given samples. The decision is that $\mathbf{v}$, when mapped into $u(\mathbf{v})$, is a member of that class to which it is closer, on the average.

In the preceding sections it has already been shown that this decision procedure results in Bayes' decisions if the transformation is linear and the probability densities of the sets of N-dimensional vectors, though different, are Gaussian. It will now be shown that if the transformation is allowed to be completely arbitrary (but piecewise continuous), then this decision rule is equivalent to Bayes' rule even for arbitrary probability densities of the classes F and G.

The decision rule intuitively derived from the above geometrical considerations, in which members of sets are clustered while sets are kept apart, can be stated by Eq. (3.24).

$$\text{Decide } \mathbf{v} \in F, \text{ if } |u(\mathbf{v}) - \overline{u_F(\mathbf{v})}| < |u(\mathbf{v}) - \overline{u_G(\mathbf{v})}|;$$
$$\text{decide } \mathbf{v} \in G, \text{ if } |u(\mathbf{v}) - \overline{u_F(\mathbf{v})}| > |u(\mathbf{v}) - \overline{u_G(\mathbf{v})}|. \tag{3.24}$$

This decision rule compares the height of the surface over the point to be classified, $u(\mathbf{v})$, with the average heights of the surface over the two sets of given samples, $\overline{u_F(\mathbf{v})}$ and $\overline{u_G(\mathbf{v})}$. The decision is made that $\mathbf{v}$ is a member of that set, F or G, to which it is closer.

If $p_F(\mathbf{v})$ and $p_G(\mathbf{v})$ are the probability densities of $\mathbf{v}$ under the assumptions that $\mathbf{v}$ is a member of class F or G, then by Bayes' rule we have

$$\text{Decide } \mathbf{v} \quad F, \text{ if } p_F(\mathbf{v}) > p_G(\mathbf{v});$$
$$\text{decide } \mathbf{v} \,\epsilon\, G, \text{ if } p_F(\mathbf{v}) < p_G(\mathbf{v}). \tag{3.25}$$

This decision rule, derived in Chapter II and stated in Eq. (2.47b), calls for deciding that $\mathbf{v}$ is a member of F if, under the assumption that F occurred, $\mathbf{v}$ is a more likely observation than under the assumption that G occurred. For simplicity, in the above rule and in the following derivation, a priori probabilities of F and G and costs of false alarm and false dismissal have been assumed equal. This, while simplifying the notation, does not influence the results appreciably.

We now show that if the function $u(\mathbf{v})$, involved in Eq. (3.24) and expressing the desire to find invariant properties of classes, is obtained as a solution of the minimization problem given below, then the geometrically motivated decision rule of (3.24) equals the decision theoretically optimum Bayes' rule of (3.25), and thus renders classificatory decisions with a minimum probability of error. The equivalence holds, of course, only in the limit as the sample size becomes large.

$$\text{Minimize } [\sigma_F^2(u) + \sigma_G^2(u)] = Q \tag{3.26}$$

if

$$\overline{u_F} - \overline{u_G} = K > 0. \tag{3.27}$$

The significance of this minimization problem is that it obtains the function u required in Eq. (3.24) by operating on a set of samples. The solution of the problem under the assumption of a certain class of polynomial transformations was already given. Here the optimum polynomial transformation of degree R which approximates the function $u(\mathbf{v})$ will be derived by minimizing the expected error (in making the approximation).

First, the rule of Eq. (3.24) will be reduced to an equivalent but simpler form. Note that if the inequalities of Eq. (3.24) hold, so do those of Eq. (3.28).

$$\text{Decide } \mathbf{v} \,\epsilon\, F, \text{ if } [u(\mathbf{v}) - \overline{u}_F]^2 < [u(\mathbf{v}) - \overline{u}_G]^2;$$
$$\text{decide } \mathbf{v} \,\epsilon\, G, \text{ if } [u(\mathbf{v}) - \overline{u}_F]^2 > [u(\mathbf{v}) - \overline{u}_G]^2. \tag{3.28}$$

Squaring both sides of the inequalities, canceling like terms, and rearranging the inequality yield Eq. (3.29).

$$u^2(\mathbf{v}) - 2u\overline{u}_F + \overline{u}_F^{\,2} < u^2(\mathbf{v}) - 2u\overline{u}_G + \overline{u}_G^{\,2}. \qquad (3.29\text{a})$$

$$\overline{u}_F^{\,2} - \overline{u}_G^{\,2} < 2u(\overline{u}_F - \overline{u}_G). \qquad (3.29\text{b})$$

$$\text{Decide } \mathbf{v} \, \epsilon \, F, \text{ if } u(\mathbf{v}) > \frac{\overline{u}_F + \overline{u}_G}{2}. \qquad (3.29\text{c})$$

This rule expresses the fact that if $u(\mathbf{v})$ is closer to $\overline{u}_F$ than to $\overline{u}_G$, as stated in Eq. (3.24), then $u(\mathbf{v})$ must lie above the midpoint between $\overline{u}_F$ and $\overline{u}_G$.

Now we solve the minimization problem of Eq. (3.26), subject to the constraint stated in Eq. (3.27). To facilitate the solution, we minimize Eq. (3.30a) subject to Eq. (3.30b) instead, and show later that the two problems have identical solutions.

$$\text{Minimize } Q' = \overline{u}_F^{\,2} + \overline{u}_G^{\,2}. \qquad (3.30\text{a})$$

$$K = \overline{u}_F - \overline{u}_G > 0. \qquad (3.30\text{b})$$

Using the method of Lagrange multipliers and writing out the expression in integral form, we obtain Eq. (3.31).

$$Q' + \lambda K = \int \Big\{ u^2(\mathbf{v}) [p_F(\mathbf{v}) + p_G(\mathbf{v})] + \lambda u(\mathbf{v}) [p_F(\mathbf{v}) - p_G(\mathbf{v})] \Big\} d\mathbf{v}. \qquad (3.31)$$

Setting the variation of Eq. (3.31) equal to zero, Eq. (3.32) is obtained.

$$\delta(Q' + \lambda K) = 0 = \int \Big\{ 2u(\mathbf{v})[p_F(\mathbf{v}) + p_G(\mathbf{v})] + \lambda [p_F(\mathbf{v}) - p_G(\mathbf{v})] \Big\} \delta u \, d\mathbf{v}. \qquad (3.32)$$

Since δu is arbitrary, however, the expression within the braces must be identically zero for all δu. Solving for $u(\mathbf{v})$, we obtain Eq. (3.33).

$$u(\mathbf{v}) = -\frac{\lambda}{2} \frac{p_F(\mathbf{v}) - p_G(\mathbf{v})}{p_F(\mathbf{v}) + p_G(\mathbf{v})}. \qquad (3.33)$$

The Lagrange multiplier may now be evaluated by substituting Eq. (3.33) in the constraint of Eq. (3.30b).

$$K = \overline{u}_F - \overline{u}_G = -\frac{\lambda}{2} \int \frac{[p_F(\mathbf{v}) - p_G(\mathbf{v})]^2}{[p_F(\mathbf{v}) + p_G(\mathbf{v})]} d\mathbf{v} > 0. \qquad (3.34)$$

We have to note only that the integral is a positive quantity, establishing the fact that the constant λ is negative. This fact permits us to rewrite Eq. (3.33) as

$$u(\mathbf{v}) = \left| \frac{\lambda}{2} \right| \frac{p_F(\mathbf{v}) - p_G(\mathbf{v})}{p_F(\mathbf{v}) + p_G(\mathbf{v})}. \qquad (3.35)$$

Substitution in the simplified decision rule, Eq. (3.29c) yields the further simplified rule of Eq. (3.36).

$$u(\mathbf{v}) > \frac{\overline{u}_F + \overline{u}_G}{2} = \left|\frac{\lambda}{4}\right| \int [p_F(\mathbf{v}) - p_G(\mathbf{v})]\, d\mathbf{v} = 0; \qquad (3.36a)$$

$$\text{Decide } \mathbf{v} \,\epsilon\, F, \text{ if } u(\mathbf{v}) > 0; \qquad (3.36b)$$

$$\text{decide } \mathbf{v} \,\epsilon\, G, \text{ if } u(\mathbf{v}) < 0. \qquad (3.36c)$$

Without loss of generality this rule states that $\overline{u}_F$ and $\overline{u}_G$ are assumed to lie, respectively, above and below zero. The separation K is maintained.

When Eq. (3.35) is substituted in the decision rule of Eq. (3.36), we obtain Eq. (3.37), which is satisfied only if $p_F(\mathbf{v}) > p_G(\mathbf{v})$, the criterion required by Bayes' rule.

$$\text{Decide } \mathbf{v} \,\epsilon\, F, \text{ if } u(\mathbf{v}) = \left|\frac{\lambda}{2}\right| \frac{p_F(\mathbf{v}) - p_G(\mathbf{v})}{p_F(\mathbf{v}) + p_G(\mathbf{v})} > 0. \qquad (3.37)$$

Thus the two rules are proved to be equivalent if $u(\mathbf{v})$ is a solution of the minimization problem stated in Eqs. (3.30a) and (3.30b). It now remains to show only that the problem stated in Eqs. (3.26) and (3.27) is equivalent to that stated in Eqs. (3.30a) and (3.30b).

It is seen from Eqs. (3.36a) and (3.27) that $\overline{u_F(\mathbf{v})} = -\overline{u_G(\mathbf{v})} = K/2$. Substituting this value in Eq. (3.26), we obtain Eq. (3.38).

$$Q = \sigma_F^2(u) + \sigma_G^2(u) = \overline{u_F^2} + \overline{u_G^2} - \overline{u}_F^2 - \overline{u}_G^2 = \overline{u_F^2} + \overline{u_G^2} - \frac{K^2}{2}. \qquad (3.38)$$

Since $K^2/2$ is a constant, the minimization of Q leads to the same solution as the minimization of Q'.

Thus the nonlinear transformation that separates members of F from those of G and yields decisions with a minimum probability of error is given in Eq. (3.37).

3.3 APPROXIMATION OF THE GENERALIZED DISCRIMINANT

The expected error in approximating $u(\mathbf{v})$ by the linear combination of an arbitrary set of functions $\phi_n(\mathbf{v})$ is given in Eq. (3.39). The squared expression is the squared error due to the approximation if the observation $\mathbf{v}$ is made, and the second bracketed expression is the probability that $\mathbf{v}$ will occur (neglecting differences in the a priori probabilities of the two classes).

$$E = \int \left[u(\mathbf{v}) - \sum_{n=0}^{R} a_n \phi_n(\mathbf{v}) \right]^2 \frac{1}{2} \left[p_F(\mathbf{v}) + p_G(\mathbf{v}) \right] \mathbf{dv}. \qquad (3.39)$$

Using variational methods, we may solve for the coefficients of combination, a_n, of the set of functions $\phi_n(\mathbf{v})$ by setting $\partial E / \partial a_s = 0$, for all $s = 0, 1, \ldots, R$.

$$\frac{\partial E}{\partial a_s} = 0 = \int \left[u(\mathbf{v}) - \sum_{n=0}^{R} a_n \phi_n(\mathbf{v}) \right] \phi_s(\mathbf{v}) \left[p_F(\mathbf{v}) + p_G(\mathbf{v}) \right] \mathbf{dv}. \qquad (3.40)$$

By interchanging the order of summation and integration and by substituting (3.37) into (3.40), we obtain (3.41). The constant $\lambda/2$ has been absorbed into the coefficient a_n.

$$\int u(\mathbf{v}) \phi_s(\mathbf{v}) \left[p_F(\mathbf{v}) + p_G(\mathbf{v}) \right] \mathbf{dv} =$$
$$= \sum_{n=1}^{R} a_n \int \phi_n(\mathbf{v}) \phi_s(\mathbf{v}) \left[p_F(\mathbf{v}) + p_G(\mathbf{v}) \right] \mathbf{dv}. \qquad (3.41a)$$

$$\int \phi_s(\mathbf{v}) \left[p_F(\mathbf{v}) - p_G(\mathbf{v}) \right] \mathbf{dv} =$$
$$= \sum_{n=0}^{R} a_{n'} \int \phi_n(\mathbf{v}) \phi_s(\mathbf{v}) \left[p_F(\mathbf{v}) + p_G(\mathbf{v}) \right] \mathbf{dv}. \qquad (3.41b)$$

By letting the integral on the left side of the equation be β_s and that on the right be $\gamma_{ns} = \gamma_{sn}$, the general element of the matrix γ, we can write (3.41) in matrix notation as shown in Eq. (3.42), where $\mathbf{b}$ is the row vector of β_s and $\mathbf{a}$ is that of a_n.

$$\beta_s = \sum_{n=0}^{R} a_n \gamma_{ns} \qquad \text{for } s = 0, 1, \ldots, R \qquad (3.42)$$

$$\mathbf{b} = \mathbf{a} \gamma.$$

The coefficients, a_n, may now be solved in Eq. (3.43) to yield the solution of the optimum linear combination of $\phi_n(\mathbf{v})$ functions that approximates $u(\mathbf{v})$ with a minimum expected error.

$$\mathbf{a} = \mathbf{b} \gamma^{-1}. \qquad (3.43)$$

In the special case in one dimension and in the case where $\phi_n(v) = v^n$ and we wish to approximate $u(v)$ with a polynomial of degree R, β_s and γ_{ns} are moments of the probability densities, as shown below.

$$\beta_s = \int v^s \left[p_F(v) - p_G(v) \right] dv. \qquad (3.44a)$$

$$\gamma_{ns} = \int v^{n+s} \left[p_F(v) + p_G(v) \right] dv. \qquad (3.44b)$$

When only a finite number of samples of F and G are available, moments of the samples can be computed, although it has not been shown whether or not the coefficients $\{a_n\}$ thus obtained still minimize the expected error. It is known, however, that as the sample size increases, this procedure becomes optimum.

In the finite sample case, β_s and γ_{ns} are given below. M_1 and M_2 are the number of samples of F and G, respectively.

$$\beta_s = \frac{1}{M_1} \sum_{m=1}^{M_1} f_m^{\ s} - \frac{1}{M_2} \sum_{m=1}^{M_2} g_m^{\ s}. \tag{3.45a}$$

$$\gamma_{ns} = \frac{1}{M_1} \sum_{m=1}^{M_1} f_m^{\ n+s} + \frac{1}{M_2} \sum_{m=1}^{M} g_m^{\ n+s}. \tag{3.45b}$$

In the case where $\mathbf{v}$ is a vector in N dimensions and we wish to approximate $u(\mathbf{v})$ with a polynomial of degree R of the form given in Eq. (3.46), the solution given above still holds formally.

$$\text{Polynomial} = \sum a_{rg \cdots t} v_1^{\ r} v_2^{\ g} \cdots v_N^{\ t} \quad \text{where } r + g + \cdots + t \leq R. \quad (3.46)$$

By letting the general term $a_{rg \cdots t} v_1^{\ r} v_2^{\ g} \cdots v_N^{\ t} = a_n \phi_n(\mathbf{v})$, we can put the multidimensional problem in the form already solved above. While in one dimension the number of coefficients of an Rth-degree polynomial is R, and the γ matrix to be inverted is $R \times R$, in N dimensions the Rth-degree polynomial approximation yields a γ matrix that is $\binom{R+N}{N} \times \binom{R+N}{N}$, requiring solutions for a large number of coefficients.

3.4 AN ILLUSTRATIVE EXAMPLE

The illustrative example of this section will show that the polynomial which successfully approximates the nonlinear discriminant may be of a rather low degree. Each of two classes, F and G, was assumed divided into two disjointed subclasses, F_1, F_2 and G_1, G_2, respectively. The subclasses were purposely arranged so that the linear techniques of the preceding chapter would fail to separate F from G. That is, we cannot fit two nonintersecting ellipses to members of F and G, and we cannot partition the plane with a line so as to separate members of F and G.

The two-dimensional sample problem shown in Fig. 3-4 does not represent physical data. Samples were constructed only to demonstrate techniques in a situation where results are easily portrayed and compared with intuition.

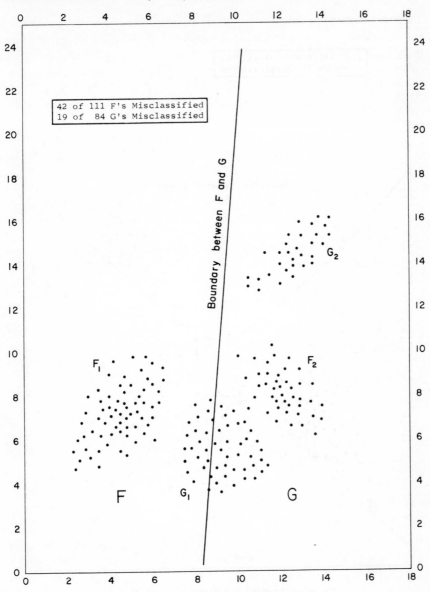

Figure 3-4. Polynomial discriminant, R = 1.

The polynomial approximation of the generalized discriminant was programmed on a digital computer and the function $u(v_1, v_2)$ was constructed for $R = 1$ through 6, where R is the degree of the polynomial. The contour $u(v_1, v_2) = 0$ separates the region where v is classified a member of F from the region where it is classified a member of G. Contours of $u(v_1, v_2) = 0$ are plotted for $R = 1, 2, 3, 4$ and 6 in Figures

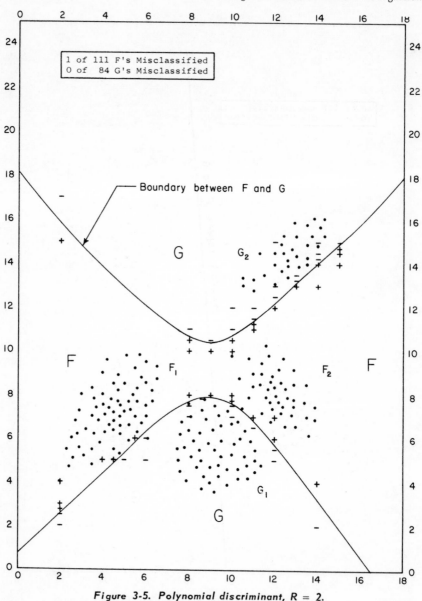

Figure 3-5. Polynomial discriminant, R = 2.

3, 4, 5, 6, 7 and 8. The boundaries were obtained experimentally by trying sample "unknowns," points denoted by + and −, and by computing $u(v_1, v_2)$ at those points by use of the decision rule "learned" by computer. The + and − signs indicate the sign of $u(v_1, v_2)$ where samples were tried

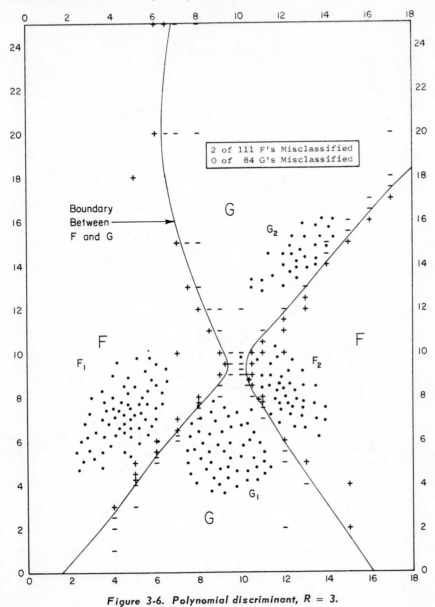

Figure 3-6. Polynomial discriminant, R = 3.

Note that the discriminant $R = 1$, shown in Fig. 3-4, is the linear discriminant already discussed in Chapter II. Since only the means and variances of the classes are known in linear discrimination, it is not surprising that the separation between F and G remains poor. As far as the discriminant is concerned, F is a single ellipsoidal cluster contain-

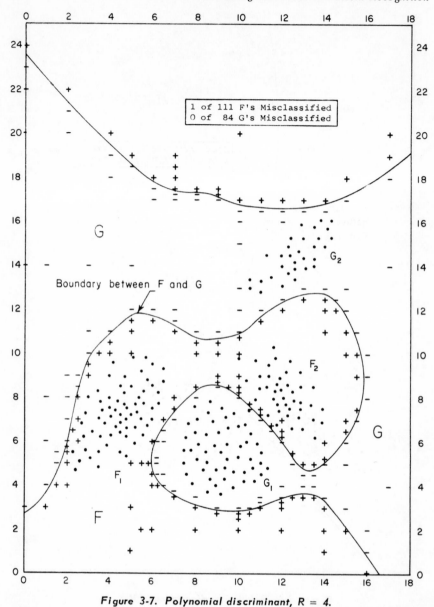

Figure 3-7. Polynomial discriminant, R = 4.

ing F_1 and F_2, while G is a more or less vertically oriented ellipse that includes G_1 and G_2. In this light, perhaps, the linear discriminant shown in Fig. 3-4 is not unexpected. This example does point out, however, that F and G are not separable by decision procedures that employ only a linear ~mbination of the input parameters. We will return to this point in the next chapter.

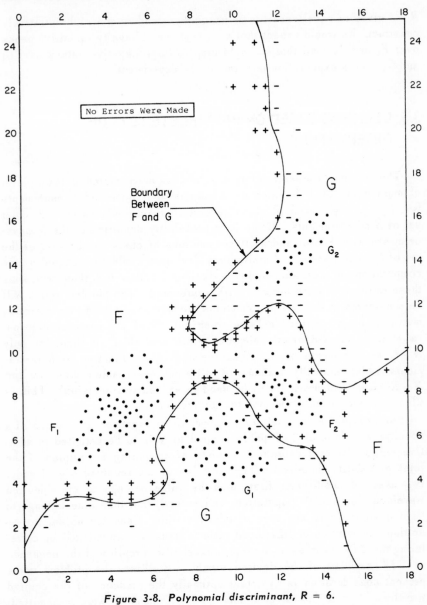

Figure 3-8. *Polynomial discriminant, R = 6.*

The boundary of decision regions constructed by use of a second-degree polynomial is shown in Fig. 3–5. It is seen that the conic section partitions the two-dimensional space so that F and G are separated without error. As the degree of the polynomial is increased to 3, 4, and 6, shown in Figs. 3–6, 3–7, and 3–8, an increasingly better fit is provided. This is particularly true in the region *between* subclasses, where

$R = 4$ gives an excellent fit to an imaginary boundary one might intuitively construct. We would expect that $u(v_1, v_2)$ would have two positive peaks over F_1 and F_2, and that it would drop to large negative values over G_1 and G_2. This expectation is borne out by experiment.

3.5 DECISIONS BASED ON INCOMPLETE SETS OF OBSERVATIONS

The problem of classificatory analysis has been treated as the problem of making the best decision on the basis of N observed measurements $(v_1, v_2, \ldots, v_N)$, as to which, of several classes, produces the particular set of N measurements. If the joint probability densities of the N measurements were known under all assumptions of class membership of the set of N measurements, classificatory decisions could be rendered by the computation of the N-dimensional likelihood ratios and then comparing these ratios with each other or with a threshold. The problem which will be considered in this section concerns the method of making the optimum, multiple, binary-choice decision when not all of the N-measurable parameters of an N-dimensional process are available. If there are only $N - K$ measurements on an object because of malfunction of K instruments which normally measure K different observables, how are the $N - K$ *given* measurements to be used in an optimum decision? This is also an important question in detection problems.

For example, in a detection problem, if the presence or absence of a specific waveform of $2TW$ product equal to N is to be detected in additive noise, optimum detection consists of comparing the values of the joint probability density of $2TW$ samples of the received signal under two assumed conditions: first, that the value belongs to the "desired waveform plus noise" population; and second, that the value belongs to "noise alone." In the case of additive white Gaussian noise, the resulting computation or likelihood ratio is usually instrumented by correlating the $2TW$ samples of the input signal with a replica of the sequence of $2TW$ samples of the desired signal. However, the problem under present consideration is to detect optimally the presence of the desired waveform if it is known that only $2TW - K$ samples were transmitted; that is, with the fact known that not all of the signal was transmitted; part of it was interrupted, jammed, or is missing for other reasons.

The question raised by this problem is: whether knowledge of the higher order densities can or cannot help to make multiple, binary-choice decisions if the measurements needed for insertion into these densities are not all actually available.

In the following discussion, several ways of utilizing knowledge of the higher order densities are explored, and the optimum method of making classificatory decisions on $N - K$ measurements is derived. The different methods of making classificatory decisions will be stated in the form of Decision Rules.

Without any loss of generality, it will be assumed in the following that the set of $N - K$ measurements may be a member of only one of two classes F or G, that the cost of deciding that the set belongs to F when indeed it is a member of G (the cost of false alarm) is c_a, the cost of deciding in favor of G when actually the set belongs to F is c_d (the cost of false dismissal).

If all the N measurements on an input were available, and c_a were equal to c_d, an eminently reasonable way of making classificatory decisions would be as follows:

$$\text{Decide } (v_1, v_2, \ldots, v_N) \text{ belongs to } F, \text{ iff } \frac{p(F|v_1, v_2 \cdots v_N)}{p(G|v_1, v_2 \cdots v_N)} > 1. \quad (3.47)$$

This decision states that if, given $v_1, v_2, \ldots, v_N$, F is more likely than G, then one should decide that the N-dimensional vector $\mathbf{v}$ belongs to F. The opposite decision is made if the inequality doesn't hold. Eq. (3.47) may be written as shown in Eqs. (3.48a) and (b), where $P(F)$ and $P(G)$ are the a priori probabilities of occurrence of classes F and G, respectively.

$$\text{Decide } \mathbf{v} \in F, \text{ iff } \frac{p(F|v_1, v_2, \ldots, v_N)}{p(G|v_1, v_2, \ldots, v_N)} =$$

$$\quad (3.48a)$$

$$= \frac{p_F(v_1, v_2, \ldots, v_N) P(F)}{p_G(v_1, v_2, \ldots, v_N) P(G)} > 1$$

or

$$\frac{p_F(v_1, v_2, \ldots, v_N)}{p_G(v_1, v_2, \ldots, v_N)} = l(\mathbf{v}) > \frac{P(G)}{P(F)} = T = \text{constant threshold.} \quad (3.48b)$$

The function $l(\mathbf{v})$ is the N-dimensional likelihood ratio. Several other likelihood ratios will be introduced later; they will be distinguished from each other by subscripts which will indicate the Decision Rule with which the likelihood ratios are associated.

Suppose that of the N-measurable parameters on which decisions would be based, only $N - K$ are available. In the following, four of several possible decision rules are discussed for deciding, from available measurements, which of the two classes, F or G, is most likely.

Decision Rule 1 (Decision Based on the Marginal Densities)

This rule states that, given the measurements $(v_1, v_2, \ldots, v_{N-K})$, decide that they belong to F if F is more likely than G as follows:

$$\text{Decide } (v_1, v_2, \ldots, v_{N-K}) \in F, \qquad \text{iff } \frac{p(F|v_1, v_2, \ldots, v_{N-K})}{p(G|v_1, v_2, \ldots, v_{N-K})} > 1. \quad (3.49)$$

This equation may be rewritten as:

$$\frac{p(F|v_1, v_2, \ldots, v_{N-K})}{p(G|v_1, v_2, \ldots, v_{N-K})} = \frac{P(F)}{P(G)} \frac{p_F(v_1, v_2, \ldots, v_{N-K})}{p_G(v_1, v_2, \ldots, v_{N-K})} > 1. \quad (3.50a)$$

Decide $(v_1, v_2, \ldots, v_{N-K}) \in F$,

$$\text{iff } \frac{p_F(v_1, v_2, \ldots, v_{N-K})}{p_G(v_1, v_2, \ldots, v_{N-K})} > \frac{P(G)}{P(F)} = T. \quad (3.50b)$$

$$\text{Let} \qquad \frac{p_F(v_1, v_2, \ldots, v_{N-K})}{p_G(v_1, v_2, \ldots, v_{N-K})} = l_1(v_1, v_2, \ldots, v_{N-K})$$

be the $N - K$ dimensional likelihood ratio, abbreviated as $l_1(v)$ to simplify the notation. This likelihood ratio is the ratio of marginal densities of the actually observed variables. Decision Rule 1 states: to determine if v should be classed in F or G, compare $l_1(v)$ with a threshold; which in effect, means that since $v_1, v_2, \ldots, v_{N-K}$ are the only measurements made, these measurements alone should be the basis for decision.

Decision Rule 2 (Decision Uses the Most Probable Values of the Missing Measurements v_{N-K+1} through v_N)

After the $N - K$ measurements $(v_1, v_2, \ldots, v_{N-K})$ are made, the probability density of the missing K measurements (v_{N-K+1} through v_N) can be calculated and their most probable values chosen for use in the N-dimensional likelihood ratio $l(v)$. The value of the ratio $l(v)$, when the most probable values of the K missing measurements are used, is $l_2(v)$. The most probable values are those which maximize the probability density given in Eq. (3.51) and are denoted by $\hat{v}$

$$p(v_{N-K+1}, v_{N-K+2}, \ldots, v_N | v_1, v_2, \ldots, v_{N-K}). \qquad (3.51a)$$

$$p(\hat{v}_{N-K+1}, \ldots, \hat{v}_N | v_1, \ldots, v_{N-K}) \geq$$

$$\geq p(v_{N-K+1}, \ldots, v_N | v_1, \ldots, v_{N-K}) \qquad (3.51b)$$

$$\text{for all } \{v_{N-K+1}, \ldots, v_N\}.$$

A possible decision rule is then the following:

Decide $(v_1, \ldots, v_{N-K}) \; \epsilon \; F$,   iff $l_2(\mathbf{v}) =$

$$= \frac{p_F(v_1, \ldots, v_{N-K}, \; \hat{v}_{N-K+1}, \ldots, \hat{v}_N)}{p_G(v_1, \ldots, v_{N-K}, \; \hat{v}_{N-K+1}, \ldots, \hat{v}_N)} \; \frac{P(G)}{P(F)} = T. \qquad (3.52)$$

This rule predicts the most likely values of the missing measurements and uses them as if they had actually been measured.

Decision Rule 3 (Decision Uses Most Probable Value of Likelihood Ratio)

When only $N - K$ measurements $(v_1, v_2, \ldots, v_{N-K})$ are made, the likelihood ratio $l(\mathbf{v})$ is a random variable, a function of the unmeasured random variables v_{N-K+1} through v_N. To indicate this fact, the random likelihood ratio is denoted by $l_3(\mathbf{v})$ which is defined in Eq. (3.53).

$$l_3(\mathbf{v}) = \frac{p_F(v_{N-K+1}, \ldots, v_N \mid v_1, \ldots, v_{N-K})}{p_G(v_{N-K+1}, \ldots, v_N \mid v_1, \ldots, v_{N-K})}. \qquad (3.53)$$

There is a probability density $p(l_3(\mathbf{v}))$ associated with $l_3(\mathbf{v})$. The most probable value of the likelihood ratio, given the observed $v_1, \ldots, v_{N-K}$ measurements, can now be chosen; that is, a decision can be based on the most probable value of the likelihood ratio $l_3(\mathbf{v})$, defined as follows:

$$p(\hat{l}_3(\mathbf{v})) \geq p(l_3(\mathbf{v})). \qquad (3.54)$$

The decision rule is to

$$\text{Decide } (v_1, \ldots, v_{N-K}) \; \epsilon \; F, \text{ iff } \hat{l}_3(\mathbf{v}) > T. \qquad (3.55)$$

Decision Rule 4 (Decision Uses Average Value of Likelihood Ratio)

In this decision rule, the likelihood ratio is again treated as a random variable $l_3(\mathbf{v})$, a function of the missing K measurements. Of course, the observed $N - K$ measurements are known parameters in $l_3(\mathbf{v})$. Instead of using in this rule the most probable value, the average value of the likelihood ratio is used, with $v_1, \ldots, v_{N-K}$ given, as a basis for deciding between F and G.

$$\text{Decide } (v_1, \ldots, v_{N-K}) \; \epsilon \; F, \text{ if } E[l_3(\mathbf{v})] > T. \qquad (3.56a)$$

$$E[l_3(\mathbf{v})] = \int_{-\infty}^{\infty} l_3(\mathbf{v}) p(l_3(\mathbf{v})) dl_3. \qquad (3.56b)$$

In certain *very seldom* occurring situations, where $l_3(\mathbf{v})$ is a monotonic function of v_{N-K+1} through v_N, Eq. (3.56b) may be written as follows:

$$E\left[l_3(\mathbf{v})\right] = \int_{-\infty} \cdots \int \int^{\infty} l_3(v_{N-K+1}, \ldots, v_N) \times$$

$$\times p(v_{N-K+1}, \ldots, v_N | v_1, \ldots, v_{N-K}) dv_{N-K+1}, \ldots, dv_N. \qquad (3.57)$$

To compare the different decision rules, the probabilities of error (both kinds) are computed so as to determine which decision results in the smallest probability of error. The two error rates, probability of false alarm and probability of false dismissal, $P(FA)$ and $P(FD)$, are given in Eqs. (3.58) and (3.59), where Y is the region of the N-dimensional space within which the decision rule in vogue decides that the set of measurements $(v_1, v_2, \ldots, v_{N-K})$ belong to F. Similarly, Y' is the region in which the decision favors class $\bar{F}$. If there are only two classes, Y' is the complement of Y.

$$P(FA) = P(G) \int_Y \int \cdots \int p_G(v_1, v_2, \ldots, v_N) dv_1, dv_2, \ldots, dv_N. \qquad (3.58)$$

$$P(FD) = P(F) \int_{Y'} \int \cdots \int p_F(v_1, v_2, \ldots, v_N) dv_1, dv_2, \ldots, dv_N. \qquad (3.59)$$

The differences between the decision rules described in the preceding arise *only* in the manner in which the region Y is selected. Hence, a subscript is used to denote the decision rule which gave rise to the choice of the region Y. For instance, Y_2 is the region in the N-dimensional space within which Rule 2 decides in favor of class F.

According to each of the decision rules, the comparison of a likelihood ratio with a threshold determines the region Y. If the ratio exceeds the threshold T, a decision is made that $(v_1, \ldots, v_{N-K}) \epsilon Y$; if the ratio is less than T, the decision is that the set of measurements belong to Y'. It should be noted that, given the values $(v_1, v_2, \ldots, v_{N-K})$, the likelihood ratios $l_1(\mathbf{v})$ through $l_3(\mathbf{v})$ are all functions of the $N - K$ given measurements alone. No matter how complicated functions the likelihood ratios may be, they are, for a specified choice of $P_F(v_1, \ldots, v_N)$ and $P_G(v_1, \ldots, v_N)$, deterministic functions of $v_1, v_2, \ldots, v_{N-K}$. The region Y, whichever rule is used, has an infinite extent in the K-dimensional manifold of the missing measurements. The integrals of Eqs. (3.58) and (3.59) may be written as shown in Eqs. (3.60) and (3.61), where the region y denotes the region of the $N - K$ dimensional space in which the measurement values are assigned to class F by the rule in vogue. Similarly, y' is the complement of y.

$$P(FA) = P(G)\int\int \cdots \int_{\gamma} p_G(v_1, v_2, \ldots, v_{N-K}) \times$$

$$\times \, dv_1, dv_2, \ldots, dv_{N-K}. \qquad (3.60)$$

$$P(FD) = P(F)\int\int \cdots \int_{\gamma'} p_F(v_1, v_2, \ldots, v_{N-K}) \times$$

$$\times \, dv_1, dv_2, \ldots, dv_{N-K}. \qquad (3.61)$$

If the positive constants c_a and c_d are the costs of false alarms and false dismissals, $p_F(v_1, \ldots, v_{N-K})$ and $p_G(v_1, \ldots, v_{N-K})$ are the marginal densities of the random processes F and G, and γ_s and γ_g are the regions in the $N - K$ dimensional subspace of measured values in which decision rules s and g, respectively, decide that the observations should belong to F, then rule s is better than g if the inequality of Eq. (3.62) holds in the specified direction. Each side of the inequality expresses the probability of error according to the corresponding decision rule.

$$P(G)c_a\int\int \cdots \int_{\gamma_s} p_G(v_1, \ldots, v_{N-K})dv_1, \ldots, dv_{N-K} \, +$$

$$+ \, P(F)c_d\int\int \cdots \int_{\gamma_s} p_F(v_1, \ldots, v_{N-K})dv_1, \ldots, dv_{N-K} \, <$$

$$(3.62)$$

$$< \, P(G)c_a\int\int \cdots \int_{\gamma_g} p_G(v_1, \ldots, v_{N-K})dv_1, \ldots, dv_{N-K} \, +$$

$$+ \, P(F)c_d\int\int \cdots \int_{\gamma'_g} p_F(v_1, \ldots, v_{N-K})dv_1, \ldots, dv_{N-K}.$$

Given the densities $p_F(v_1, \ldots, v_{N-K})$ and $p_G(v_1, \ldots, v_{N-K})$, obviously the decision rule which minimizes Q is best (minimizes the probability of error).

$$Q = P(G)c_a\int\int \cdots \int_{\gamma_s} p_G(v_1, \ldots, v_{N-K})dv_1, \ldots, dv_{N-K} \, +$$

$$+ \, P(F)c_d\int\int \cdots \int_{\gamma'_s} p_F(v_1, \ldots, v_{N-K})dv_1, \ldots, dv_{N-K}. \qquad (3.63)$$

Since y'_s is the complement of y_s, Q can be written as in Eq. (3.64).

$$Q = P(F)c_d + \iint \cdots \int_{y_s} [P(G)c_a p_G(v_1, \ldots, v_{N-K}) -$$

$$- P(F)c_d p_F(v_1, \ldots, v_{N-K})]dv_1, \ldots, dv_{N-K}. \qquad (3.64)$$

We already showed in the preceding chapter that Q_{min} occurs if y_s is the region in which the integrand is always negative, where Eq. (3.65) holds.

$y_{optimum}$ where $c_d P(F)p_F(v_1, \ldots, v_{N-K}) >$

$$> c_a P(G)p_G(v_1, \ldots, v_{N-K}). \qquad (3.65)$$

For the special case where $c_a = c_d$, the region y_{opt} is determined and hence class F is selected when

$$\frac{p_F(v_1, v_2, \ldots, v_{N-K})}{p_G(v_1, v_2, \ldots, v_{N-K})} > \frac{P(G)}{P(F)}. \qquad (3.66)$$

We recognize that this is just the decision made by the marginal densities of Decision Rule 1.

As these results apply to the two types of problems given at the beginning of this section, we may conclude that:

1. The optimum classificatory decision on the $N - K$ observed measurements consists of comparing the ratio of probability densities of the actually observed $N - K$ measurements with a threshold. No useful purpose is served by knowing to what higher dimensional process the $N - K$ measurements belong.

2. In the optimum detection of a known signal in noise, where it is known that only part of the signal was transmitted, it is best to correspondingly truncate the stored reference signal and correlate the input with the truncated reference. No prediction of the missing portions of the waveform should be employed.

3.6 RECOGNITION IN NOISE

The preceding mathematical developments were based on the assumption that sets of noise-free samples of the classes are given and that membership determining functions must be developed from these samples. There are many practical instances, however, when noise-free samples of the category are not available. In these instances the observed differences between samples are not solely caused by genuine, permissible variants of the class, but are affected by the corrupting influence of noise. In the classification of waveforms of 5 zero crossings, for example, the presence of noise may cause a change in the number of zeros, a fact that has serious consequences in learning the correct category definition. In another example of practical interest, this effect is even more pronounced. Consider the automatic recognition of the acoustic signals caused by a given type of motor vehicle and its differentiation from those of other types. The situation may arise in which the vehicle types of interest may be observed only in a noisy environment in which many types of systematic and random noises corrupt the desired signals. These noises affect the decision regions determined by the learning process and thus result in an incorrect definition of the category.

It will be remembered that all the methods discussed so far apply to the following problem: Given a finite set of samples of two or more populations of signals of unknown probability densities, find a decision procedure that separates the populations from one another with minimum error. Thus we see that recognition of noisy signals fits well within the framework of the problem already treated. If the two or more sets of signals, on which the decision rule is based, are "noisy" members of the classes to be recognized, the procedures discussed will learn to differentiate between noisy samples of one class and those of another.

Quite a different situation exists, however, if learning is done on uncorrupted samples of a class, but events to be classified exist only in a noisy environment. When the noise environment at the time of learning and at recognition differ, we are faced with a difficult problem. In mathematical terms the problem is that we were given sets of signals with one set of probability densities and we are trying to determine in which of these would fit inputs drawn from signals of another set of probability densities. If noise is additive, the new probability densities are the convolutions of the densities of "noise free" signals and that of "additive noise."

The degrading influence of corrupting noise is illustrated qualitatively in Fig. 3-9. Here the probability of error (2 classes and equal a priori probabilities are assumed) is shown plotted against the additive noise power. The dotted curve indicates the error of recognition obtained when the decision regions are always chosen optimum for the current noise power. This implies that we relearn classification at each noise level. For large additive noise, the error rate becomes 0.5, equivalent to guessing, as we might expect. For no additive noise, $\sigma_N^2 = 0$, the error rate settles down to a low value. The upper curve, drawn with a solid line, indicates the error rate when the decision rule, optimum at a noise level σ_L^2, at which recognition was learned, is employed on inputs immersed in noise of a different noise level, σ_N^2. Note that the two

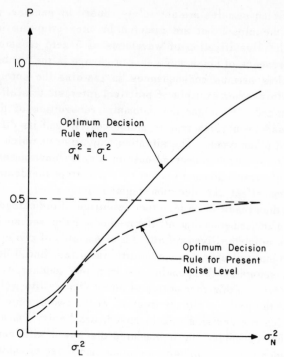

Figure 3-9. Probability of error as a function of noise power.

rules are the same at σ_L^2, where the noise associated with current inputs equals that present when recognition was learned.

The evaluation of the degradation suffered when recognizing noisy signals is difficult and can only be done numerically for specific cases. Gaussian processes immersed in additive Gaussian noise is the only case for which an analytic solution has been obtained. The difference between the two error curves was expressed and its derivatives with respect to σ_N^2 were investigated near σ_L^2. For the above case, the two error curves were tangent to each other at σ_L^2, thus leading to the conclusion that decision performance is not seriously affected by small deviations of the noise level from that present when learning, at least in recognizing Gaussian processes in Gaussian noise.

3.7 DECISIONS BASED ON A FINITE NUMBER OF SAMPLES

The classical problem of testing statistical hypotheses or making classificatory decisions involves making multiple-choice decisions when the statistical properties of the classes about which the observations are made are known. The statistical properties are assumed known in the form of the probability densities associated with the distributions of members of the various classes.

The application of decision theory to pattern recognition may take either of two forms. In one, where sufficient knowledge exists about the nature of the distribution of the set of observable parameters in the observation space, the probability densities are actually known, thus satisfying the fundamental requirements necessary in the making of multiple-choice decisions. When the probability densities are not known for physical or other reasons, however, this knowledge must be gained by taking samples of the classes. Although it is possible to estimate—at least in certain cases—the number of samples sufficient to characterize the classes adequately, in many cases a large enough number of samples is not available for the construction of the probability densities required for the statistical treatment of the classification problem. Hence a way must be found for making optimum classificatory decisions based on a small number of samples.

The purpose of this section is to show how a solution that minimizes the cost of incorrect decisions on a finite number of samples can be obtained. The problem is stated and solved only in its one-dimensional form.

If we observe a random variable v, which may belong to either of two random processes F or G characterized by probability densities $p_F(v)$ and $p_G(v)$, the optimum decision rule (that which minimizes the cost of misclassification) requires that we test the variable v to see if it is contained in an interval of v where $p_F(v)$ is larger than $p_G(v)$ or in one where the reverse is true. For simplicity, again equal costs and a priori probabilities are assumed. The boundary that separates decisions favoring class F from those favoring class G is given by the locus of points where $p_F(v) - p_G(v) = 0$.

If we had a function $u(v)$ which was positive over the intervals of v where $p_F(v) > p_G(v)$ and negative elsewhere, the optimum decision would be given by Eq. (3.66).

$$\text{Decide } v \in F, \text{ if } u(v) > 0;$$
$$\text{decide } v \in G, \text{ if } u(v) < 0.$$
$$(3.66)$$

Earlier in this chapter the optimum function $u(v)$ was obtained. Its approximation, computed from samples of F and G, was given in the form of a polynomial. The solution obtained there guaranteed minimum probability of error only for a large number of samples. The problem considered in this section deals with the optimum placement of the zero crossings of $u(v)$ when the number of samples is small.

Problem

Assume that M members of two classes F and G are given. Of these, M_F belong to class F and M_G belong to class G. Let us assume that a member of a class is a one-dimensional random variable which may assume any value between $-\infty$ and $+\infty$. The two classes may be two different one-dimensional random processes with arbitrary probability densities, and the M_F and M_G samples of the two processes may be finite but independently chosen samples.

Suppose that a decision procedure which can distinguish between members of F and those of G is to be constructed as a binary valued function of v, ($f(v)$ has values of ±1) and the decision is made to

$$\text{decide } v \, \epsilon \, F, \text{ if } f(v) = +1;$$

$$\text{decide } v \, \epsilon \, G, \text{ if } f(v) = -1.$$

Also suppose that the function $f(v)$ is permitted to have only Z or fewer zeros in order to limit the complexity of the resulting equipment. The problem to be solved can be stated as follows.

If c_A is the cost of a false alarm and c_D is the cost of a false dismissal, where should the Z or fewer zeros of $f(v)$ be placed to minimize the total cost incurred by using the decision rule?

The total cost is $c = c_A N_A + c_D N_D$, where N_A is the number of alarms, or the number of samples of G misclassified as F, and N_D is the number of F's misclassified as G's.

Let R be the number of intervals on v. An interval is defined as a region of v in which one or more members of a single class are contained. In Fig. 3-10, for instance, $R = 6$, $M_F = 10$, and $M_G = 14$. To facilitate the description of the solution, additional definitions must be made.

Define K_F as the number of F intervals (intervals that contain only members of F), and K_G as the number of G intervals. In the figure below $K_F = 3 = K_G$. Note that $|K_F - K_G| \leq 1$ always. Let $n_p(F)$ be the number of samples in the pth interval. The argument F denotes that the samples of the pth interval are members of class F.

(a) If the number of zeros Z of the binary function $f(v)$ satisfies the inequality $Z \geq R - 1$, the zeros can always be located on the line v so that the cost $c = 0$; i.e., so that no errors in classification decisions are

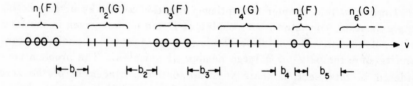

Figure 3-10. Finite number of samples of two classes.

made. $R - 1$ of the zeros should be located in the $R - 1$ boundary regions. The remaining $Z - R + 1$ zeros should be located at very high or very low values of v, where they do not influence the decisions made on the given samples. A boundary region, denoted by b, is a line segment that terminates on a sample of class F at one of its ends and on a sample of class G at the other end. A boundary region contains no samples of either class.

(b) If $Z < R - 1$, no error-free decisions can be made on all given samples. The best that can be achieved, therefore, is to place the zero crossings of $f(v)$ so that the cost is minimized. An algorithm is presented below for achieving the objective described. Steps of the algorithm are as follows.

Step 1. Temporarily locate a zero of $f(v)$ in every boundary region of the R intervals. Thus a total of $R - 1$ zeros are temporarily introduced. If decisions were made using the function $f(v)$ so obtained, no decision errors would be made. There are, however, $R - 1 - Z$ excess zeros in the resulting solution. We must, therefore, eliminate at least $R - 1 - Z$ zeros to obtain a satisfactory solution. The result of locating $R - 1 = 5$ temporary zeros in the example above is illustrated below by the encircled numbers.

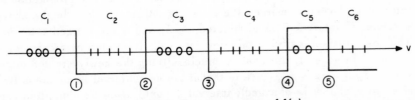

Figure 3-11. *Temporary zeros of* $f(v)$.

Step 2. Assign a cost to each interval equal to the cost of misclassifying every element of the interval. Such a misclassification would come about if the temporary zeros bounding the interval were eliminated during the attempt to reduce the number of excess zeros of the temporary function $f(v)$. Let the cost of misclassification of the pth interval be c_p. If the pth interval contains elements of class F, $c_p = c_D n_p(F)$, if it contains elements of G, $c_p = c_A n_p(G)$.

2.1. If $R - Z - 1 = 1$, remove the temporary zeros (or zero) bounding the interval corresponding to the minimum c_p. Let c_m be the minimum c_p and the corresponding interval be m.

2.1.1. If m is an end interval, remove one zero, obtaining a function $f(v)$ with exactly Z zeros.

2.1.2. If m is not an end interval, as is the case in the figure if $c_A = c_D$, remove two zeros (4 and 5 in the example), obtaining an optimum solution of $Z - 1$ zeros of the function $f(v)$. In either case, note that a minimum cost solution results.

2.2. If $R - Z - 1 = 2$, and c_m is not an end interval, remove the two zeros bounding interval m to obtain a solution with exactly Z zeros.

2.2.1. If $R - Z - 1 = 2$, and c_m is an end interval, the two cases described in (a) and (b) below may exist.

(a) The costs of the two extreme intervals c_1 and c_R are the two smallest costs and $c_1 + c_R < c_T$ where c_T is the third smallest cost of all intervals. If this is true, remove the first and last zeros, yielding a solution with exactly Z zeros and minimum cost.

(b) If alternative a above is false, then c_s, the second smallest cost block is an internal block (not c_1 or c_R) and removal of the two zeros bounding c_s yields a minimum cost solution of exactly Z zeros.

2.3. If $R - Z - 1 \geq 3$, at least two intervals must be eliminated. First remove the interval corresponding to the minimum cost c_m by removal of the zero (or zeros) that bound it. The number of excess zeros, after this step is completed, is still equal to or greater than one. We proceed to Step 3.

Step 3. In Step 2.3 above, one interval was eliminated but the required solution has not yet been obtained. The modified tentative function $f(v)$ still has a number of zeros in excess of Z. The elimination of interval m, however, merges the intervals adjacent to m. In the above example, if interval 5 is eliminated, 4, 5, and 6 are merged into one. The cost of misclassifying this new interval, illustrated below, is $c_4 - c_5 + c_6$. In general, the cost of misclassifying the newly created interval is $c_{m-1} - c_m + c_{m+1}$. Note that if the new interval is misclassified (i.e., sign of $f(v)$ is changed), interval 5 would again be classified correctly. This accounts for the minus sign of c_5. Therefore, in Step 3 we reassign costs of misclassification to the intervals as they now exist. We thus find the state of affairs identical to that which existed before the removal of any of the zeros. That is, we have $R' < R$ regions with the associated costs of misclassification, and $Z < R' - 1$. Hence the algorithm continues the iterative removal of excess zeros by executing the applicable step of steps 1 through 3 on the new arrangement of regions until the required number of zeros are removed.

A special case arises when the cost associated with more than one interval is the same and equal to the minimum cost, c_m. In this case, if

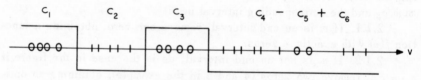

Figure 3-12. Modified cost structure.

the three steps of the algorithm would still permit a nonunique method of eliminating intervals, the interval that, after its merger with its neighbors, results in a new interval of smallest cost is to be eliminated. If Step 2.3 is applicable, the interval that, when eliminates, reduced the number of zeros most, is to be absorbed into its neighbors.

Three illustrative examples of the algorithm will now be given.

Example 1. Consider 13 samples of class 0 and 14 samples of class X given and distributed along v as shown, and we wish the optimum solution with 2 zeros or less if $c_D = c_A$.

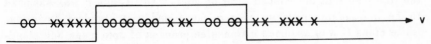

Figure 3-13. Optimum solution Z = 2.

The sequence of costs are 2 5 7 3 4 6, and 5 zeros are necessary for a solution with no error. The number of excess zeros is $R - 1 - Z = 3$, and we apply Step 2.3 and reassign costs according to Step 3 to obtain the new sequence of costs 3 7 3 4 6, a solution that has 4 zeros or 2 excess zeros. The total cost of decision thus far is 2. We now follow the special procedure above, and eliminate the interval cost 3 with the most zeros. This is the middle 3, since elimination of the end 3 would still leave an excess zero. The final solution of 2 zeros is thus shown below. The cost of decisions is 5, since an additional 3 was accumulated in this last step.

The solution can be shown in a shorthand notation given below. Here the cost incurred by the last step, the cumulative cost of all the steps, and the interval cost structure of every step in the algorithm are shown, together with the number of zeros of the temporary function and the number of surplus zeros we must still eliminate.

Cost of this Step	Cumulative Cost	Interval Cost Structure	No. of Present Zeros	Excess Zeros
0	0	2 5 7 3 4 6	5	3
2	2	3 7 3 4 6	4	2
3	5	3 8 6	2	0

Example 2. Three or less zeros of the function $f(v)$ are desired.

Figure 3-14. Optimum solution Z = 3.

Cost of this Step	Cumulative Cost	Interval Cost Structure								No. of Present Zeros	Excess Zeros
0	0	2	3	2	4	3	6	2	5	7	4
2	2	2	5		3	6	2	5		5	2
2	4	2	5		3		9			3	0

Example 3. A digital computer was programmed to execute the steps of the algorithm for the optimal placement of Z zeros on the line v. The algorithm was then applied to find the optimal discriminant function that separates members of class F from those of G by placing Z zeros on the line v so that the cost of error be minimized. Class F was assumed to be a Gaussian process of zero mean and unit standard deviation, while class G was assumed a Gaussian process of zero mean and standard deviation equal to three. For simplicity of illustration, the two processes were assumed to have equal a priori probabilities and equal costs of false alarm and false dismissal. The optimum discriminant should have two zero crossings at ± 1.648 (where the two probability densities are equal) and should be positive (deciding in favor of F) between the two zeros. This is illustrated in Fig. 3-15.

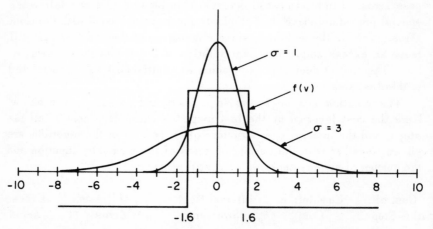

Figure 3-15. Discriminant separating Gaussian processes.

Samples of two Gaussian processes were generated on a computer. One hundred samples of both processes were used, and initially fifty seven temporary zeros of the discriminant were found. The required number of zeros of the solution was then reduced, step by step, and the cumulative cost and the cost of each step was computed. As expected, the cost of each optimum solution for decreasing values of Z increased from zero, first gradually, later more rapidly. When the required number of zeros of the solution was set equal to two (the correct value), the location of zeros was ±1.59 as compared to the theoretical value of ±1.648.

In the following paragraph the contents of this chapter are briefly summarized. Pattern detection, finding the invariant characteristics of members of a class, has been considered as the geometrical problem of minimizing the mean-square distance between members of a class after a transformation of the vector space. The ideas presented in Chapter II were extended and the class of allowable transformations in the above minimization problem was enlarged to include nonlinear transformations. Discriminant analysis, started in Chapter II, was similarly extended and its relationship to decision theory was illustrated, paralleling the development of the preceding chapter. Practical approximation of the generalized discriminant as an expansion in harmonic functions or polynomials was derived so that the expected error that results from the approximation should be minimum. The application of the approximation to a two-dimensional classification problem was described. The method of making decisions on a subset of the measured observations was shown to be optimum if decisions are based on the marginal probability densities of the measurements (i.e., on only the subset of measured observations). A qualitative discussion of learning and recognition in noise was given, showing that small changes in the noise level do not appreciably affect the decision errors. The chapter was concluded with the description of a decision procedure, optimum when only a small number of samples of the classes are available.

CHAPTER 4

Approximate and Adaptive
Techniques of Classification

In the preceding chapters analytic approximations of probability densities or discriminant functions were computed from a finite number of samples representing classes. As a general rule, the computational complexity of the methods increased as more general distributions were fitted with increasingly better approximations. In many practical instances, particularly in applications where learning in real time is an important requirement, approximations to the probability densities of class populations may be desired by nonanalytic means. That is, we must consider algorithms or simple computational procedures that construct, from a finite number of given samples, the boundaries of decision regions in the vector space. For the most part in this chapter we will be concerned with schemes that partition the space into regions by constructing boundaries that envelop the known set of samples of a class and exclude from their interiors the samples of other classes. The desired boundaries are illustrated in Fig. 4-1, where the multiply connected domains C_1 and C_2 contain the samples of the classes F and G and form boundaries not unlike those we would expect to be constructed by likelihood ratio computers. Members of F are dense in C_1 and those of G are dense in C_2; thus we expect to decide that any point in the interior of C_1 is a member of F, while points in the interior of C_2 are members of G.

In this chapter we will consider methods that construct boundaries exhibiting the above described desired characteristics. The methods will be motivated by decision theoretic considerations (comparison of probability densities). Emphasis will be placed on the simplicity of the computations that must be performed and on the speed with which they

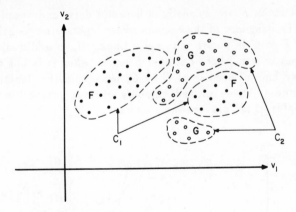

Figure 4-1. Desired boundaries of F and G.

can be performed. A class of machines will be introduced that select or compute a small number of "typical" samples from the sets of large numbers of given samples of the classes. The Perceptron, an illustrative example of neural nets, is briefly discussed, and the use of cascaded or multilayered machines is explored as a means of performing complicated operations as a cascade of simpler operations.

4.1 A SIMPLE ALGORITHM FOR CONSTRUCTING DECISION REGIONS

We will now consider a simple decision rule that constructs regions from a finite number of samples. The region corresponding to a class contains all known samples of that class. The decision rule is given below.

Decide that the input vector is a member of class F if it is nearer to the nearest known member of F than to the nearest known member of G.

Extended to the case where inputs may belong to an arbitrary number of classes, this decision rule assigns a point to that class which has one of its given points at a shorter distance to the input than the distance between input and any given point of any other class. We will refer to this rule as the "proximity algorithm," for it assigns class membership to inputs on the basis of their proximity to known inputs. The locus of points equidistant from the nearest members of two or more classes forms the decision region boundary. This is shown in Fig. 4-2, where given samples of class F are symbolized by solid dots, and samples of G by circles. The boundary of the regions where inputs are recognized as belonging to F or G is shown with solid lines. If, in addition, we decide that an input is a member of neither F nor G, when it is not sufficiently near to any known member of F or G, we obtain the decision regions shown dotted. These closed contours enclose regions in which the known samples of the classes are populous.

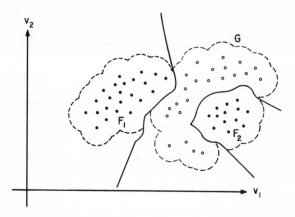

Figure 4-2. Decision regions by the "proximity rule."

One might interpret the above proximity algorithm as a method of deciding class membership on the basis of similarity to the most similar known sample of the classes. One would expect that such a rule would produce desirable results whenever members of different classes occupy disjointed regions in the vector space. It is also obvious that the shapes or numbers of the regions in which samples are contained are quite arbitrary and do not influence the success achievable with this rule.

The method of measuring nearness, in the above rule, is not as critical as in the preceding chapters, for now we measure distance to each of a number of points that are spread out over the region in which members of the classes are contained. Since simplicity motivates the development of approximate techniques (techniques that are not *analytic* approximations of likelihood ratio computers), distance might as well be measured with the easily computed Euclidean distance measure. We will see that this yields an additional advantage in cases where not all N measurements on the physical world are available.

The analytic expression of the decision rule is given in Eq. (4.1a), where $\mathbf{f}_m$ is the mth member of class F and $\mathbf{g}_s$ is the sth member of class G. The minimum is taken from among all choices of m and s. This rule is written in Eq. (4.1b) to exhibit the computations that must be carried out.

$$\text{Decide } \mathbf{v} \in F, \text{ if } \min|\mathbf{v} - \mathbf{f}_m| < \min|\mathbf{v} - \mathbf{g}_s|. \tag{4.1a}$$

$$\text{Decide } \mathbf{v} \in F, \text{ if } \min\left[\sum_{n=1}^{N}(v_n - f_{mn})^2\right] < \min\left[\sum_{n=1}^{N}(v_n - g_{sn})^2\right]. \tag{4.1b}$$

It will be recalled from Section 3.5 that classification decisions should be based on the $N - K$ dimensional marginal probability densities when only $N - K$ input measurements are available. Thus the optimum decision is made when, in the decision procedures, we completely ignore the coordinate values of given samples in the dimensions of the space where measurements on the present input are lacking. If the kth dimension is lacking, for instance, the decision rule is given in Eq. (4.2).

$$\text{Decide } \mathbf{v} \in F, \text{ if } \min\left[\sum_{n \neq k}^{N}(v_n - f_{mn})^2\right] < \min\left[\sum_{n \neq k}^{N}(v_n - g_{sn})^2\right]. \tag{4.2}$$

This rule is readily computed from the known samples by the omission from the summation of those terms that correspond to the missing input coordinates. By a similar argument, inputs can be stored as given samples even if some of their dimensions are lacking. During recognition, those terms that correspond to missing dimensions of either the input or of the stored references must be omitted from the summation in Eq. (4.2).

4.2 APPLICATION TO SPEAKER RECOGNITION

The proximity algorithm of the preceding section has been used as part of an extensive program aimed at establishing the feasibility of constructing a machine that can recognize any one of a large number of speakers, regardless of the text they speak. Of the many facets of this program only those will be discussed that pertain to a practical application of the above algorithm.

For the purpose of clarifying the illustration about to be given, we must very briefly review the human speech generating mechanism. As a rough approximation, humans are said to utter "voiced" and "unvoiced" sounds. Voiced sounds include most of the vowels, while unvoiced sounds contain most consonants. During the utterance of voiced sounds, the human speech generating mechanism can be approximated by the block diagram of Fig. 4-3. This consists of a generator of approximately triangular shaped pulses feeding several band-pass filters with center frequencies variable over somewhat overlapping ranges. The pulse repe-

tition frequency, commonly called pitch frequency, is largely responsible
for the pitch of the human voice, while variations in the tuned frequencies
and amplitudes of the four resonant circuits serve to form the various
vowel sounds we utter. For this reason, the four resonant frequencies
are called formant frequencies. During the utterance of unvoiced sounds,
a different model employing a noise generator must be used.

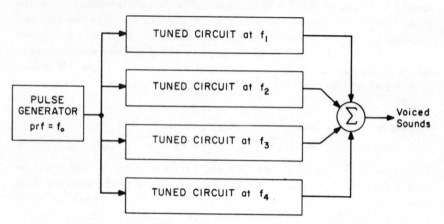

Figure 4-3. Model for generating "voiced" sounds.

It is evident, from the preceding, that human speech can be characterized parametrically (at least during the utterance of vowel sounds) by the
sequence of instantaneous values that the network variables assume as a
function of time. Such parametric descriptions of human speech have
formed the bases of many investigations throughout the last twenty years
or so. It is also evident that if speech can be characterized parametrically, so can the characteristics that account for the speaker's identity.
It was postulated, therefore, that sounds uttered by one speaker (as
characterized by any suitable parametric description) are not identical,
most of the time, to sounds uttered by another. Anatomical and other
differences assure the discriminability of speakers. In the four-dimensional space of the four formant frequencies, for example, it was postulated that different speakers would have different probability densities.

Researchers have found that a different region corresponds to each
vowel sound in the four-dimensional formant frequency space and that
these regions are fairly disjointed. Thus the probability density of vowel
sounds uttered by a speaker is expected to contain many separated peaks;
sounds produced by a speaker are expected to lie in a multiply connected
domain. Sounds uttered by another speaker are also expected to lie in a
multiply connected domain with considerable overlap between the do-

mains of the two speakers. This is a typical situation where we would expect linear discriminants or best fitting Gaussian probability densities to *fail* to separate sounds of different speakers. We would have to employ the nonlinear techniques of Chapter III or their nonanalytic approximation presented in the form of the proximity algorithm. In the experiment described below the proximity algorithm was employed.

Sample voiced sounds were collected from several speakers. Each pronounced the same two sentences in his normal tone of voice. From these sentences four-dimensional vector representations of voiced sounds were extracted by the simultaneous sampling of the four formants. Samples were taken at 20 m sec intervals. This is illustrated in Fig. 4-4 which shows the "instantaneous" spectrum of speech as a function of time. The amplitude of the spectrum corresponds to the intensity of the intensity modulated display, the 0 to 5 kc band of frequencies is plotted vertically, and time progresses from left to right.* Voiced intervals of speech are readily recognized by the presence of regularly spaced vertical lines of high intensity. These correspond to the individual pulses emitted by the pitch pulse generator in the model of Fig. 4-3. The four formant frequencies, or tuned frequencies of the resonant circuits, are the four peaks of the spectrum through which, for the sake of emphasis, lines have been drawn as a function of time. A voiced sound-sample is represented by the set of four frequencies to which the resonant circuits are tuned at the same instant of time.

All of the approximately one hundred voiced sound-samples collected from two sentences were used to construct the sample population of each speaker. Each of the speakers subsequently spoke a number of *different* sentences. The texts of these differed drastically from the text of the two sentences from which the sample populations were drawn. Only 8.7 per cent of the voiced sound-samples from these sentences were misclassified as regards the speaker who uttered them. If we wish to recognize the identity of the speaker, decisions would, of course, be based on a number of independent voiced sound-samples and a considerable improvement in error rate could be achieved. Although speaker-to-speaker and sound-to-sound variations of human speech are not statistically random phenomena, it is apparent, nevertheless, that no difficulty is encountered in recognizing the identity of the speaker with the proximity algorithm, if several seconds of his speech are available. In several seconds, a large number of statistically independent voiced sounds are uttered.

---

*This Figure was made available through the courtesy of Mr. C. P. Smith of the U. S. Air Force.

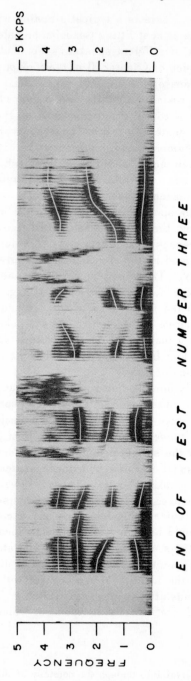

Figure 4.4. Parametric representation of human speech.

4.3 ALGORITHM FOR APPROXIMATING LIKELIHOOD RATIO COMPUTATIONS

One of the shortcomings of the proximity algorithm of Section 4.2 is its sensitivity to "odd" samples, or noisy observations. A stray and not representative sample of a class falling in the midst of members of another class can create a small annulus about itself that can be the source of many classification errors. This can be overcome by devising schemes that take into account not only the nearest sample to the point to be classified, but also the relative numbers of samples in all classes; that is, all samples that are near. Decisions are thus based on a local majority rule, a procedure that is in good agreement with likelihood ratio computations.

Of the many ways in which a local majority rule can be stated, the two statements below exhibit interesting but different properties. In the first of these, given in Eq. (4.3), a small but nonzero distance between the input,

$$\text{Decide } \mathbf{v} \,\epsilon\, F, \text{ if } \sum_{m=1}^{M_F} \frac{1}{d^k(\mathbf{v}, \mathbf{f}_m)} > \sum_{s=1}^{M_G} \frac{1}{d^k(\mathbf{v}, \mathbf{g}_s)}. \tag{4.3}$$

$\mathbf{v}$ and the sth member of class G may be outweighed by a larger number of members of F that may not be quite so near to $\mathbf{v}$. The exponent, k, determines the size of the neighborhood of $\mathbf{v}$ that influences the decision, while the distance measure, $d(\ )$, is the Euclidean distance. This decision rule still maintains a small annulus about an isolated point, but the annulus may be made small.

The alternate statement of a local majority rule is given in Eq. (4.4), where r is the radius of the effective neighborhood that influences decision making. For sufficiently high values of k, this rule essentially counts the number of F samples contained within a radius of r from $\mathbf{v}$ and compares this number with the number of samples of G within the same neighborhood.

$$\text{Decide } \mathbf{v} \,\epsilon\, F, \text{ if } \sum_{m=1}^{M_F} \left[\frac{1}{1 + \left(\dfrac{d(\mathbf{v}, \mathbf{f}_m)}{r}\right)^k} \right] > \sum_{s=1}^{M_G} \left[\frac{1}{1 + \left(\dfrac{d(\mathbf{v}, \mathbf{g}_s)}{r}\right)^k} \right]. \tag{4.4}$$

It should be noted that the expression in the brackets is the same as that which describes the frequency (amplitude) response of a low-pass Butterworth filter. The latter is unity below and zero above the cutoff frequency.

The above local majority rule overcomes the noise or stray-sample-sensitivity of the proximity algorithm. It is apparent that, as the sample size approaches infinity and r approaches zero, the above modified proximity algorithm renders Bayes' decisions.

4.4 A MACHINE FOR SELECTIVE SAMPLING AND RECOGNITION

It is seen from Fig. 4-2, and it was observed from the low error rates obtained in practical problems, that the proximity algorithm, or its modification discussed in the preceding section, indeed constructs decision regions of the most arbitrary shape and complexity. A practical limitation of the algorithm is that its storage requirements are not bounded, but depend on the number of available samples from which the machine must learn to recognize membership in classes.

We might consider the problem, therefore, of judiciously selecting a limited number of samples from those we encounter during learning to retain as "representative" members of their classes. The samples that must be selected and stored must be distributed in the same region of the space as that from which the larger set of given samples are obtained. They must be typical or representative samples that yield, by use of the proximity algorithm or by use of another simple decision rule, decision boundaries very much like those obtained by use of the larger number of given samples. A graphical illustration of this requirement is given in Fig. 4-5, where points represent the large set of given samples from which a smaller sample set is constructed to cover the same region of the space. Members of the small sample set are indicated by the symbol **x** and their number must be less than the storage limitation imposed on the solution.

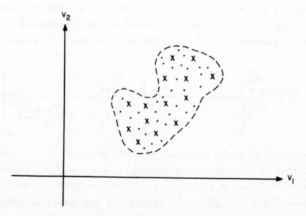

Figure 4-5. Selective sample set construction.

The selection of the small set of samples, given the large set of samples of class F and G, can be stated mathematically in a number of different ways, depending on the properties desired of the solution.

We may wish to construct a sample set containing exactly k samples so that up to the lth moment the sample moments should equal the moments of the probability density that actually describes the distribution of samples in the N-space. The constant k, of course, is related to l. This procedure of selecting samples assures that the small sample distribution resembles that of the large sample set. It requires, however, that the large sample set be given *before* the small sample selection can begin, since sample selection requires that the large sample distribution be fully known.

Another statement of the sample set construction problem requires that exactly k samples be chosen so that the least-squares error between the decision regions to be approximated and the region formed by the proximity algorithm be minimized. The algorithm uses only the k samples that are to be selected. In this procedure we require that the regions generated by the algorithm operating on k samples approximate, as closely as possible, the regions generated by the much larger sample set.

The practical requirement of constructing the selected sample set in an adaptive manner may serve as the basis for a third alternative. Samples can be selected so that they "best" approximate that portion of the population of sample vectors which was observed up to the present time. As each new sample is introduced, the choice of selected samples is updated or modified, so that it "best" represents the enlarged set of samples observed thus far. Of the several methods of accomplishing the above objective, this one will be described in the next section.

It is evident from the preceding discussion that a number of procedures can be developed which sort out the superfluous samples from those that are given and reduce the number of stored samples with which a given population of vectors can be represented. The chosen samples are, in a sense, the typical samples of the class; they are the samples to which all members of the class must be similar. Membership in the class is thus measured by similarity to at least one of the set of selected typical samples. The class of machines that operate according to these principles will be called "Machines for Selective Sampling and Recognition."

4.5 ADAPTIVE SAMPLE SET CONSTRUCTION

Several methods of selecting samples adaptively from a given population of vectors can be envisioned. The method discussed in this section is motivated by two considerations, both of which are aimed at the end objective of achieving machine learning and recognition rapidly. The first of the two considerations is that updating the decision rule, incorporating the effect of a newly introduced sample of the class into the decision making process, should be accomplished simply and with a minimum of computation. The second consideration in evolving the adaptive sample set construction technique is that the decision rule itself be simple and should be applicable rapidly.

To achieve these two objectives, strict adherence to decision theoretical procedures must be sacrificed. At the same time, however, the departure from decision theory can be kept to a minimum. The adaptive procedure described below represents a compromise between the theoretical objective of achieving a minimum error probability and the engineering objectives of instrumentability and simplicity.

Let us consider the given sample population to be represented by the union of normally distributed subpopulations, where each of the latter can be represented by its mean and variance. This is illustrated in Fig. 4-6, where the region occupied by members of class F is approximated by the union of circles that represent equiprobable contours of Gaussian processes. For simplicity, these are shown to have equal variances in all directions and are assumed to have uncorrelated variables.

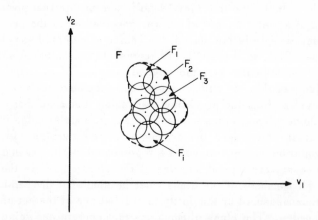

Figure 4-6. Class F, the union of Gaussian processes.

The decision that the vector $\mathbf{v}$ be termed a member of F rather than G can be written as in Eq. (4.5). In this equation the basic decision, "given the set of observations described by the vector $\mathbf{v}$, is F more likely than G?" is transformed into the evaluation and comparison of sums of joint probability densities. K_F and K_G are the number of F and G subclasses, and $p_{Fi}(\mathbf{v})$ is the conditional probability density of subclass F_i. This is expressed in Eq. (4.6).

$$\frac{P(F|\mathbf{v})}{P(G|\mathbf{v})} \gtrless 1; \qquad \frac{P(F|\mathbf{v})}{P(G|\mathbf{v})} = \frac{P(\mathbf{v}|F)\,P(F)}{P(\mathbf{v}|G)\,P(G)} = \frac{\displaystyle\sum_{i=1}^{K_F} P(F_i)\,p_{F_i}(\mathbf{v})}{\displaystyle\sum_{j=1}^{K_G} P(G_j)\,p_{G_j}(\mathbf{v})} \gtrless 1. \qquad (4.5)$$

$$p_{F_i}(\mathbf{v}) = \frac{1}{(\sqrt{2\pi}\,\sigma)^N} \exp\left(-\frac{\displaystyle\sum_{n=1}^{N} [v_n - m_n(F_i)]^2}{2\sigma^2}\right). \qquad (4.6)$$

Since the a priori probability of class F_i is proportional to M_i, the number of samples in subclass i, the decision rule can be written as in Eq. (4.7). Here M_i is the number of samples in subclass F_i, M_j is the number of samples in subclass G_j, v_n is the nth coordinate of the input, $m_n(F_i)$ and $m_n(G_j)$ are the nth coordinates of the means of F_i and G_j, respectively, and σ^2 is the variance of the subclass. The constant C is the ratio of the costs associated with the two kinds of decision errors.

$$\text{Decide } \mathbf{v} \in F, \text{ if } \quad \sum_{i=1}^{K_F} M_i \exp\left(-\frac{\displaystyle\sum_{n=1}^{N} [v_n - m_n(F_i)]^2}{2\sigma^2}\right) >$$

$$> C \sum_{j=1}^{K_G} M_i \exp\left(-\frac{\displaystyle\sum_{n=1}^{N} [v_n - m_n(G_j)]^2}{2\sigma^2}\right). \qquad (4.7)$$

In the decision rule given in Eq. (4.7), all but a few of the terms are essentially zero. If the input $\mathbf{v}$ is near the mean of the ith subclass of class F — that is, if $\mathbf{v}$ is near the center of the ith circle in Fig. 4-6 — then only those terms that have means near $\mathbf{m}_i$ contribute significantly to the lefthand side of Eq. (4.7). The numerical value of the lefthand side of the equation is a measure of the number of F samples near $\mathbf{v}$, weighted according to their distances from $\mathbf{v}$. The righthand side of the equation similarly expresses the number of samples of G near $\mathbf{v}$. The comparison of the measures of the numbers of samples of F and G near $\mathbf{v}$ is a qualitative approximation of the likelihood ratio computation.

The selection of the set of points $\mathbf{m}_i$ and $\mathbf{m}_j$, the means of the F and G subclasses, can be approximated by a step-by-step adaptive procedure.

The procedure does not guarantee that the optimum choice of subclass means is made, but experimental evidence indicates that low error probabilities are obtained with this procedure.

Let us consider construction of the sample set step by step, assuming that the memory of the machine is empty at the start of the procedure. We will introduce vectors that represent members of class F or G. The adaptive sample set construction machine will be informed of the correct class membership of each of the sequentially introduced vectors. As its objective, the machine will approximate the probability densities of the introduced samples by the unions of Gaussian densities of variance σ^2, and it will automatically find the location of the means of these subclasses. These means form the sample set the machine stores together with the a priori probabilities of the subclasses. Decision making, in the form of recognition of any new input as a member of F or G without human intervention, is accomplished by the decision rule of Eq. (4.7).

When the first input is introduced, assuming that it is a member of F, it is assigned to subclass F_1 and is assumed to be its mean. The sample is stored as m_{F_1} and the number of samples of F_1, the number M_1, is also stored. The latter has the value one. The second input (assume that it also belongs to F), is now introduced. If it is within a threshold distance F of m_{F_1}, it is assigned to F_1, m_{F_1} is updated (the mean of the two samples is computed), and M_1 is changed to two. If, on the other hand, the input is not within a threshold distance T of m_{F_1}, it is assigned to F_2 and is assumed to be its mean, m_{F_2}. It is then put in storage together with M_2, the number of occurrences of F_2. The latter number is one.

Assume that the third input is a given member of G. The input is stored as the mean of G_1 and the number of G_1 occurrences is set to one. During the construction of the sample set, this procedure is continued. It results in the generation of a set of points which represent the locations of clusters of inputs. The size of the clusters is approximately T. The threshold is arbitrarily chosen but will generally be of a magnitude on the order of σ.

The sample set construction procedure results in the storage of only one point for all samples that lie inside a spherical cluster of approximate size T. The number of samples within this cluster is stored as the a priori probability of the subclass.

When the sample set construction process is completed, the decision rule of Eq. (4.7) can be applied to any new input event to decide if it is a member of F or G. Although this procedure was illustrated for the case when inputs could be members of only two classes, it is equally applicable when membership in more classes is possible.

The adaptive sample set construction process is illustrated in Fig. 4-7. Here the input v of known classification C_v is introduced and its distance to each stored vector of class C_v, is computed. Let each such stored vector be $\mathbf{m}_k$. The smallest distance, d_s, and the subclass membership of the corresponding stored vector, C_s, are noted.

If d_s is larger than T, then the input is not close enough to any existing subclass of class C_v. Hence a new subclass must be started. This is accomplished by storing the vector as the mean of a new subclass, tagging it with the known classification of the input vector, C_v, and storing the fact that one occurrence of the new subclass has been observed. If a total of x subclasses have occurred so far, $\mathbf{v}$ will be stored as $\mathbf{m}_{x+1}$, the mean of the $x + 1^{\text{st}}$ subclass. This procedure is summarized in the flow-chart of Figure 4-7.

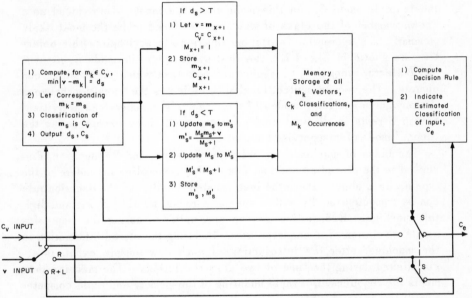

Figure 4-7. Adaptive sample set construction.

If d_s is less than T, there is at least one subclass of class C_v to which $\mathbf{v}$ is sufficiently close. Update the mean of the closest subclass, $\mathbf{m}_s$, and increase M_s, the number of past occurrences of the subclass, by one. In the figure, the new values of the stored quantities M_s and the vector $\mathbf{m}_s$ are denoted by M'_s and $\mathbf{m}'_s$, respectively.

Recognition is accomplished by evaluating the decision rule of Eq. (4.7) at the point $\mathbf{v}$, the input, and by indicating the classification estimate, together with the relative probability of class membership.

During the adaptive sample set construction procedure we might say that the machine is "learning." The machine learns to characterize classes by the selection of "typical" samples from a larger collection of samples that are introduced sequentially. During this mode, labeled L in Fig. 4-7, the input vector, $\mathbf{v}$, and its known classification, C_v, are introduced to the machine. The appropriate switching functions are indicated on the figure.

During the recognition mode, the machine operates without human intervention, that is, without knowledge of the class membership of the input. Operations in this mode, labeled R, consist of the evaluation of the decision rule at the point v.

As mentioned earlier, in Chapter II, after a satisfactory level of performance is achieved, the machine may be left to its own devices and may be permitted to "learn" without supervision by a human. This is accomplished by first recognizing the input as a member of one or another of the classes, while the machine is in mode R, and then switching to the learning mode L. In this mode the same input is introduced as a known member of the class of which it was found to be the most likely member. The appropriate switching functions to accomplish this objective are shown in Fig. 4-7. The first switch sets the mode L, R, or R and L (learn, recognize, recognize and learn), in which the machine can operate. The second switch, labeled S, indicates the transition between the recognize and learn modes of the machine's unsupervised activities. Switch S rests in the indicated position at all times except during the "learn" mode of unsupervised activities.

The class of machines for Selective Sampling and Recognition, discussed in the preceding section, can employ a sampling procedure of the type outlined above. It can be instrumented readily and the decision rule can be computed rapidly with a special-purpose, hybrid (analog and digital) machine. Recognition can be accomplished during the time of a single revolution of a magnetic drum. Updating the stored information in the machine, after the introduction of each new sample event, is accomplished during the time of two drum revolutions. The machine thus meets the requirement of rapid updating of the memory and rapid computation of the decision. Storage limitation is accomplished indirectly, since there are only a finite number of neighborhoods of size T (the size of a cluster) in a finite-dimensional space of finite volume. This is the type of vector space that would be obtained in cases where inputs are the results of measurements made by devices of finite dynamic range. A practical illustration of the adaptive sample set construction process is given in the next section.

4.6 APPLICATION OF ADAPTIVE SAMPLE SET CONSTRUCTION TO SPEAKER RECOGNITION

An example illustrating the application of the previously described adaptive sample set construction technique will be given in this section.

An IBM 7090 general-purpose digital computer was programmed to implement adaptive sample set construction in accordance with the flow chart given in Fig. 4-7. The use of the resulting sample set in the recognition and classification of new inputs, Eq. (4.7), was also programmed.* The technique was applied to the machine-learned recognition of speakers, a problem of moderate complexity where the probability densities of speakers' sounds are known to be multimodal.

A simple model of the human speech generating mechanism is described in Section 4.2. There the instantaneous spectra of human speech are represented by their first four major spectral peaks called formant frequencies. In the four-dimensional space in which coordinates are the formant frequencies, the sequential observation of the set of four formants can be thought of as a point that moves in the space as a function of time. Differences in speaker characteristics can be observed in the differences in the regions of the four-dimensional space in which the points that represent the speech of different speakers are moving. It should be noted that there are a number of characteristics of human speech other than the locations of the formant frequencies that are useful in speaker recognition. For illustrative purposes, here only the use of formants will be discussed. The approximate position of the point in the four-dimensional space is indicative of what the sound means, while speaker variations in the utterance of a given sound manifest themselves in relatively small variations in the position of the sound within a small neighborhood. Speaker characteristics are also exhibited in the manner in which the point, representing the instantaneous sound, moves about as a function of time. The point may transit one region of the space rapidly while it may linger in another.

The set of four formant frequencies sampled fifty times per second was extracted from the continuous speech of several male speakers. Speaker recognition, using the adaptive sample set construction algorithm, was learned from two phonetically balanced sentences spoken by each speaker. Identification of the speaker from new speech, using the decision rule of Eq. (4.7), was based on formant measurements made over a period of time, T.

Although many experiments involving a number of speakers were conducted, the adaptive sample set construction technique is best illustrated in experiments involving pairs of speakers. With the aid of the technique already described, characteristics of two speakers were "learned" by the adaptive construction of their sample sets. Speaker recognition, the determination of the more probable of the two speakers, was made by computing a likelihood ratio at each of the fifty sampling instances per sec-

---

*Although not described here, on contract AF 30(602)-2499 the additional capability of making decisions on incomplete sets of observations was included in the program.

ond. The likelihood ratio of the nth instant, $l(n)$, is the ratio of the right and left hand sides of the inequality of (4.7). Assuming equal a priori probabilities and equal costs of false alarm and false dismissal, $C = 1$ in Eq. (4.7), speaker recognition is made by comparing $l(n)$ with 1.

For a specific choice of a neighborhood of size T, when decisions were made at each sampling instant—based on just 20 msec of speech —the probabilities of error were those given in Fig. 4-8. While speaker A spoke, the computer decided 40.2 per cent of the time that the speaker was speaker B. The computer's decision was based on an examination of only the last 20 msec of the speaker's speech. Under identical conditions, while speaker B spoke, the computer decided only 4.4 per cent of the time that the speaker was A. Decisions were in error 27.3 per cent of the time.

When decisions were based on the set of four formant frequencies sampled several times during the period of decision making, T, considerable reduction in the probabilities of error were obtained, as expected. Optimum decision making based on K independent sets of observations is made by a comparison of the *product* of the likelihood ratios of the independent observations with a threshold (1 in this case). Statistical independence of the sampling instances was assured by taking samples not more frequently than the syllabic rate (about 5 syllables per second). Thus, with reasonable certainty, not more than one sample per syllable was taken. When the total observation time was 1 second, 31.2 per cent of the time A was mistaken for B and 1.1 per cent of the time B was mistaken for A. The computer was in error a total of 15.8 per cent of the time.

When the interval of speech on which decisions were based was lengthened to 2 seconds, A was mistaken for B 21.5 per cent of the time while B was never mistaken for A in 188 decisions. The computer made the wrong decision a total of 10.6 per cent of the time. When a smaller value of the constant T was chosen, no confusions between the two speakers were made even after only 1 second of speech.

The probability of error as a function of the number of independent observations can be computed if the likelihood ratio of each observation is known.[*] The relationship between the error probability and the likelihood ratio of specific observations is given in Eq. (4.8), where l_p is the likelihood ratio of the pth observation and $v_1, v_2, \ldots, v_K$ are the set of K four-dimensional vectors representing the K instantaneous sounds that comprise the set of statistically independent observations.

---

[*] A. H. Nuttall, "Error Probabilities Conditioned on Specific Observations," Litton Systems, Inc., Internal Memo, December 20, 1961.

$$P(\text{error}|\mathbf{v}_1, \mathbf{v}_2, \ldots, \mathbf{v}_K) = \frac{1}{1 + \displaystyle\prod_{p=1}^{K} l_p}. \tag{4.8}$$

In the special case where each likelihood ratio has the same value, the probability of error based on K independent observations can be shown to be related to the probability of error based on a single observation by Eq. (4.9), where $P_n(\text{error})$ is the probability of error of decisions based on n observations, and $P_1(\text{error})$ is that based on a single sample. This equation is plotted in Fig. 4-8 for several values of P_1. For a single sample error probability of 0.4, eleven observations are required before a less than 1 per cent error rate is obtained. In the event that the single sample error probability is 0.3, only six observations are required, while an error probability of 0.2 on single samples necessitates only four observations for the achievement of less than 1 per cent decision errors.

$$P_n(\text{error}) \approx \frac{P_1{}^n}{P_1{}^n + (1 - P_1)^n}. \tag{4.9}$$

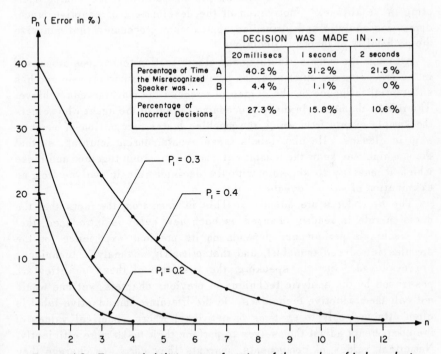

Figure 4-8. Error probabilities as a function of the number of independent observations.

	DECISION WAS MADE IN ...		
	20 millisecs	I second	2 seconds
Percentage of Time A the Misrecognized Speaker was... B	40.2 %	31.2 %	21.5 %
	4.4 %	1.1 %	0 %
Percentage of Incorrect Decisions	27.3 %	15.8 %	10.6 %

In general, of course, the likelihood ratios of different observations are not equal and the above simple formula cannot be used to predict the probability of error as a function of the number of observations used in decision making. Yet, this formula gives some insight into the potential improvement achievable through lengthening the decision time.

It is noteworthy to add that computations were performed by the general-purpose computer at approximately 2 to 3 times real time.

4.7 BIONICS, NEURAL NETS, ADAPTIVE NETWORKS, AND PERCEPTRONS

In the preceding chapters we have attempted to place certain aspects of decision making and machine learning in pattern recognition on an analytical basis. As the computational complexities and the storage requirements of the classification methods increased, adaptive methods were introduced so that results similar to those achievable with analytic techniques could be obtained with simple computational procedures operating in "real-time." Motivation of the development of adaptive procedures was analytic and strived to approximate procedures that minimize the probability of incorrect decisions.

Although the machine learning and classification techniques discussed in the preceding are automatic, the human plays an important role and has substantial influence on the degree of success the machine can achieve. The role of the human in these procedures is that of the agent who selects the sample events from which the machine learns recognition of membership in classes. He also labels these events, during learning, so that the machine may know the samples it must try to group together and those which it must try to separate with the decision rule it evolves from an examination of sample events.

The procedures are adaptive. This is seen from the facts that the decision rule is readily changed as each new event is introduced, that the machine's performance depends on its previous experience (on the samples introduced thus far), and that primarily nonanalytic techniques are employed. Strictly speaking, the first two of these qualities are possessed by the analytic technique of previous chapters, yet one would not call them adaptive techniques. In the literature the adaptive label is often attached only to systems or networks, where numerical values of the components adjust themselves to perform their tasks more efficiently. Numerical values of components, currents they carry, or charges they hold, must vary and adapt themselves as conditioned by the environment in which the system is placed. In the same sense, in the sample set construction procedures outlined earlier in this chapter, the selected typical samples of the classes are chosen adaptively. The samples chosen are adapted to the environment from which samples could be drawn.

The adaptive systems discussed in the literature, however, are entirely different and are also differently motivated. Although there are some systems based on other considerations, most adaptive systems find their origins in hypothetical models of certain human functions. Biological knowledge (or assumptions) of human mechanisms serve as the initial spark from which electronic models are conceived. Learning from nature through the application of biological assumptions to electronics is wide-spread and is practiced by many researchers who work in the field now termed "Bionics." The human nervous system, its redundant use of components, the distributed nature of human memory, and many of its other known or assumed features are modeled to a greater or lesser degree, by various electronic systems. The existing or contemplated models are too numerous to be discussed here. A partial list of references included in this volume illustrates the extent of the literature on this and allied subjects.

A typical and well-known sample of the line of investigation that bases electronic machine design on the simulation of human character-istics is a class of machines called Perceptrons. Since a number of the systems do not differ significantly from the Perceptron, we will use it as an illustration of neural nets and of adaptive and self-organizing systems.

A simple Perceptron is a machine that can be illustrated symbolically in the diagram of Fig. 4-9. In its simplest form it consists of an array of sensory units (S units), often thought of as an array of photocells which view the visual field. Sensory units are randomly connected to a set of so-called associative units (A units) that produce an output if a

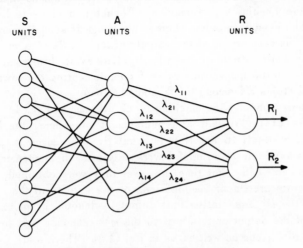

Figure 4-9. A simple Perceptron.

sufficient number of the sensory units that supply it are activated. Weighted combinations of associative unit outputs constitute a response that indicates whether or not the input sensed by the sensory units belongs to a certain category. Each input category is assigned a response unit, R, and the output of each such unit is, in general, a different linear combination of the associative unit outputs. The coefficients of linear combination are denoted by λ's.

Let us assume that the human user of this machine wants to teach it to recognize and distinguish two classes of visual images. For the sake of illustration, assume that these are "handwritten A's" and "handwritten B's," respectively, and that R_1 is the response unit assigned the A's, while R_2 is assigned the B's. A correct response is obtained if R_1 yields a larger output than R_2 when the input is an A, or R_2 exceeds R_1 for an input image that is a B. The response is considered to be in error if the reverse of these two alternatives exists.

Teaching of the machine commences by the introduction of a selection of A and B samples. A human observer watching the machine's responses determines, after each response, whether the machine decision was correct or not. The human can do this since he knows the true label (A or B) that is associated with each sample. If the machine decision is correct ($R_1 > R_2$ if the input is an A, or $R_2 > R_1$ if it is B), the human "rewards" the machine by increasing those weights (λ's) that contribute to the output of the correct response unit. If the machine decision is wrong ($R_2 > R_1$ when the input is an A), the human "punishes" the machine by reducing the weights that contribute to the incorrect decision.

Proceeding in this manner, the machine is presented with a sequence of A and B samples and is "taught" to recognize A's and B's by the reward and punishment instruction it receives from a human instructor who monitors the machine's performance. When the machine is left to make its own decisions, it decides whether the image it sees is more likely an A than a B by comparison of the outputs of R_1 and R_2.

Several modifications of these basic ideas exist. Interconnections between the A units and various rules for implementing the reward or punishment functions are among these modifications.

If we only consider the machine block diagram of Fig. 4-9 and ignore the details of the reward and punishment procedure, the Perceptron readily lends itself to scrutiny by analytic procedures. Clearly, the machine is available to do useful work only after disengagement from its human teacher. After that time, however they were obtained, the output response units are linear combinations of the outputs of the associative units. If the ith associative unit output is denoted by a_i and the contribution of the output of this unit to the mth response unit by λ_{mi}, then the output of R_m can be written as in Eq. (4.8). The λ's are weights that measure the amount of contribution of the ith associative unit to the mth

$$R_m = \sum_{i=1}^{N} a_i \lambda_{m\,i} = \mathbf{a} \cdot \lambda_m \qquad (4.10)$$

response, and their numerical values are modified, during learning, by the mechanism of reward and punishment. The expression in Eq. (4.8) is recognized to be the dot product or correlation coefficient between the vector **a** and the internally stored vector λ_m. Since the associative unit outputs are dependent only on the input image, the N associative unit outputs can be regarded as the N coordinates of the input vector **v**. In the terminology and notation used throughout this volume, the Perceptron outputs are equal to the projections of the N-dimensional input vector onto a set of stored reference vectors. Decisions are thus based on a comparison of different linear combinations of the input vector coordinates. The optimum choice of linear combinations that result in a minimization of the probability of decision errors was discussed in Chapter II. The procedure for choosing the linear combinations in the Perceptron is adaptive and results, in general, in a different linear combination from that derived in Chapter II. Although not optimum, the technique has certain advantages in that it does not require the performance of numerical computations.

A more severe limitation of the Perceptron is that it is a linear machine. It was already pointed out in Chapter III that decisions based on linear combinations of the input variables lack the ability to recognize and separate classes when classes occupy other than simply connected, disjointed, and convex regions. A more detailed discussion of the limitations of decision methods is given in Chapter V, where the subtleties are discussed and interpreted geometrically. Correlation with stored references can distinguish from each other only classes whose members are already highly clustered and where classes are already separated from each other.

In addition to the decision making aspects of the Perceptron, we must also consider the role of the human in the method of introducing samples and in the mechanism by which the machine is taught. In the analytic techniques of preceding chapters, known samples of the classes were collected by humans and were given to the machine, clearly labeling each sample in accordance with the known class-membership of each sample. Although somewhat obscured by the reward and punishment procedure, essentially the same role is played by the human in the Perceptron and a number of other devices.

The human first selects the samples he will use while teaching the machine and then selects the order in which he will introduce the samples. The order in which the samples are introduced affects the ultimate machine performance in adaptive systems; it is of no consequence in analytic techniques.

Although the human does not attach a label to each sample as it is introduced to the Perceptron, a label nevertheless becomes attached to samples as a result of the process of reward and punishment. If the machine's decision is correct, and the human monitor of machine performance rewards the machine, a label is essentially attached to the input, informing the machine of the correct class membership of the input sample. If the machine decision is in error, it is so informed by the human through the act of punishing the machine for its error. A label of "nonmember" is thus attached to the sample. It is obvious that the optimum use of known samples is to give the machine all the information available about them and not prejudice or bias the machine by selecting the order in which the samples are introduced. If the order conveys information (such as the relative importance of the samples), this information can be transmitted to the machine through the mechanism of providing it with *statistically representative* samples. Sequential introduction of samples, on the other hand, limits the storage requirements of the machine, for information contained in each sample is digested as the sample is introduced.

From the above discussion it can be concluded that adaptive techniques have advantages as well as disadvantages with respect to analytic techniques. Among the advantages are the ability to consume information with a limited storage requirement placed on the adaptive machine, the relatively high speed with which learning or updating can be affected, and the simplicity of the computations which must be performed. Among the disadvantages (at least for linear machines) can be counted mostly the inability of the machine to learn any but the simplest distributions of points. These distributions, however, are just those for which computation of the optimum decision rule presents no serious problem either.

The general criticism leveled against neural nets, adaptive processes, and the like has held the basic tenet that, given the same method of representing the world with a mathematical model (the vector space) and the same samples from which to learn recognition of the common patterns, decision theoretic methods can lead to error probabilities that are lower than those obtained by other methods. This does *not* mean that neural nets and adaptive processes should not be investigated, for there are valid reasons justifying such research. The criticism does suggest, however, that models that may be appealing from a biological point of view should be submitted to analytical scrutiny to discover if the class of decision rules that can result from the machine is indeed general enough to make the research worthwhile.

4.8 MULTILAYERED (CASCADED) MACHINES

The methods of classification described in the preceding chapters are deterministic. Given a set of samples of a category or sets of samples of several categories, the machine's performance can be determined exactly. In the concluding section of this chapter the utilization of already learned concepts or classes in a multilayered machine will be described. This will result in machine performance on a set of inputs that is not predictable solely from knowledge of the machine's circuit diagram and samples of the class in question.* As a result of exposure to a set of samples, the machine forms a "concept" of the class through the construction of the transformation that exhibits the invariant characteristics of the class, those characteristics that account for the similarity of members of the class. Membership in the class is measured with this function. Suppose, for example, that the category "square" has been learned by the presentation of a set of sample squares; and, as a result, probability of membership in the class of things called squares, or "squareness," can be expressed quantitatively. One can now consider the introduction of the function that measures "squareness" as a new dimension of the vector space. Squareness is a new measurable property of the environment; it is a test that has a quantitative outcome of the same general type as the tests on the environment performed by the original N dimensions of the vector space. An interesting consequence of introducing an already learned concept (squareness) as a new dimension of the vector space is that the vocabulary of the machine is thereby enlarged. The machine is able to describe its environment in a language that depends on the machine's previous experience. Presented with the same set of samples on which to learn a given class, two identical machines with different prior experiences will react in different ways. In some respects this is a phenomenon not unlike that which we observe in human behavior.

Except in machines where basic decisions are made by linear techniques, such as by the comparison of linear combinations of the input variables, the introduction of already learned concepts or classes as new dimensions of the vector space can enlarge, in general, the type of distributions of inputs the machine can recognize as members of the same class. This will be illustrated below where it will be shown that the same decision procedure (the same class of functions) operating on already learned concepts results in a decision procedure that corresponds to operation on the original vector space with procedures belonging to a more general type. Assume, for the sake of illustration, that the basic decision procedure consists of fitting the experimentally observed sample events with the best fitting quadratic form. The measurement of the mean-square error (Euclidean distance) between the input, **v**, and the mean of a class k already learned, m_k, is the simplest such procedure. The distance of **v** to a class k, expressed by d_k of Eq. (4.9) is the quan-

---

*It is still predictable, of course, if the complete past history of the machine's experience, or the contents of its storage, is known.

titative measure of membership in class k. Introducing membership in each of C classes as new dimensions of the space (either as added to the original dimensions or as their replacements) generates a new vector space. Dimensions of this new space are quadratic forms in the observed parameters, and the decision rules (quadratic forms) of the new space are fourth-degree polynomials of the original measured parameters. This is expressed in Eq. (4.10), where $d_k(\mathbf{v})$'s are the learned concepts quadratic forms of the original vector space, and the new decision rule (quadratic form of the learned concepts) is denoted by D.

$$d_k(\mathbf{v}) = d(\mathbf{v}, \mathbf{m}_k) = \sum_{n=1}^{N} (v_n - m_{kn})^2. \qquad (4.11)$$

$$D(\mathbf{v}) = \sum_{k=1}^{C} [d_k(\mathbf{v}) - t_k]^2 = \text{fourth-degree polynomial on } \mathbf{v},$$

$$\text{where } t_k\text{'s are constant.} \qquad (4.12)$$

The cascaded or multilayered machine implied by the procedure of introducing already learned concepts as new dimensions of the space is illustrated by the block diagram given in Fig. 4-10. Here elementary classes 1 through C are learned by use of best fitting quadratic forms $d_1(\mathbf{v}), d_2(\mathbf{v}), \ldots, d_C(\mathbf{v})$. These classes may express simple physical properties such as "roundness," "squareness," "redness," etc. Elementary classes are learned by exposure to a number of known round, square and red objects from which the common attributes of members of a class and distinguishing attributes of different classes are learned by use of procedures discussed in the preceding chapters. Although in this illustration only quadratic forms are used, the common attributes of members of a class do not have to be expressed as quadratic forms. The original observations (dimensions of the vector space) which are truly the only observations made on the physical world are the quantities $v_1, \ldots, v_N$.

Elementary classes thought of as dimensions of a C-dimensional vector space permit the machine to represent the physical world (although still viewed in terms of the quantities $v_1, \ldots, v_N$) by means of meaningful quantities $d_1, \ldots, d_C$. This representation permits the machine to use a vocabulary of descriptors such as "roundness," "squareness," "redness," etc. Quadratic forms of vectors formed of $d_1, \ldots, d_C$ are fourth-degree polynomials of $v_1, \ldots, v_N$, thus enlarging the class of functions with which an arbitrary distribution of sample events of a class may be fitted in the original vector space. Additional multilayered

Primary
Measurements
(Dimensions of
the Vector
Space)

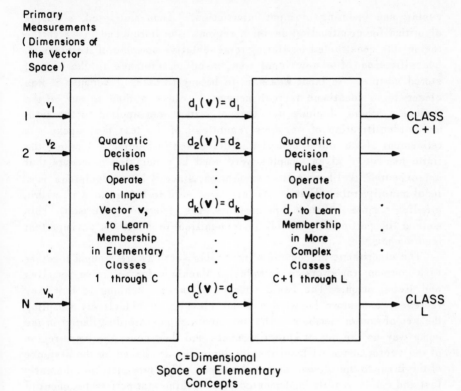

C = Dimensional
Space of Elementary
Concepts

Figure 4-10. A multilayered machine.

machine operation will further enhance the class of distributions that can be fitted in the original space.

Multilayer machines employing linear combinations of their inputs (correlators with stored references) cannot achieve improved performance, for linear combinations of linear combinations are still only linear combinations of the inputs. Multilayered linear machines are still only linear machines that can, at best, only approximate linear discriminants. This can only result in the generally inadequate procedure of partitioning the vector space into two parts by a hyperplane.

Pattern detection and recognition techniques discussed in this chapter differ from those of preceding chapters, for the most part, in the statement of the objectives they attempt to achieve. Within certain constraints limiting the permissible complexity of the resulting machine, in earlier chapters we strived to characterize classes and recognize their members so that the probability of making wrong decisions should be minimized. In this chapter we developed techniques that approximate those of preceding chapters by use of methods that inherently result in rapid processing and updating of input information. Thus motivated, a simple algorithm for constructing decision regions was introduced in which the region was constructed by storing representative samples of the classes. Classification of a new input was based on distance to the nearest stored sample. An input was said to belong to class *A* because it was closer to at least one typical member of class *A* than to any of the typical members of class *B*. This algorithm was applied to the automatic identification of speakers regardless of the text they spoke. A refinement of the above method was discussed in Section 4.3, where the finite number of given samples were used in a decision procedure that approximated likelihood ratio computation, since it based decisions on a local majority rule. That is, an input was said to belong to *A* if, within a radius *r*, more *A* than *B* type samples were observed in the past. This method is particularly useful if recognition in noise is an important requirement.

The algorithmic procedures of preceding sections are brought together in a common framework by introducing Machines for Selective Sampling and Recognition. The basic concept of these machines is that they represent and store knowledge about classes by selectively sampling the set of known members. The selected samples are distributed in the same way as the set of known members and they cover the same region of the vector space. Classificatory decisions are based on the distance of the input to the closest selected sample. This procedure is inherently fast and can be readily implemented by a machine that performs sequential comparisons with stored samples. A specific way of performing selective sampling with an adaptive technique is described next. The advantage of this technique is that it uses input information as it occurs and, as it is influenced by the new sample, it updates the stored information concerning the nature of the decision regions. An illustration to speaker recognition is given.

Not decision theoretically motivated adaptive techniques are illustrated with a discussion of the Perceptron. Mathematical and geometrical interpretation of the systems aspects of the Perceptron is given, and the idea of using cascaded simple machines to recognize more complex classes is briefly described.

CHAPTER 5

Some Practical Problems
in the Solution of Pattern
Recognition Problems

In the foregoing chapters we dealt with the problems of learning how to recognize membership in classes once classes were represented as N-variate random processes. From a finite number of representative samples of the classes, generalized discriminant functions or estimates of probability densities were constructed and decisions were made with a minimum cost to the decision maker. Underlying basic assumptions were made about the sufficiency of the vector space to contain the information that allows classification, assumptions were made about the representativeness of the samples from which class membership was learned, and about the adequacy of the class of machines within which the optimum solution was sought.

In this chapter we will consider the problem of applying the methods previously discussed to the practical solution of pattern recognition problems. We will consider the problems that must be solved when, in a physical problem, we must decide which of the methods to apply, how to choose dimensions of the vector space, and how to choose the coordinate values and their ranges.

There are two different cases of practical interest. In one we are given two or more ensembles of N-dimensional vectors and we are asked to examine each of the ensembles so that we may decide which computational procedure should be used to learn class (or ensemble) membership of a vector. We must also decide how many and which specific vectors should be selected as representative of those on which we wish to learn. It is assumed that we have no a priori knowledge or have no way of finding any physical or mathematical relationship between the variables used in the vector representation of events of the physical world.

In the second problem of practical interest, we are given an actual physical or engineering problem. It is up to us to choose the number of samples, the variables, and the method of learning class membership. The considerations affecting these choices in practical problems are discussed in this chapter. A geometrical interpretation of a number of decision procedures is given so that capabilities and shortcomings of the procedures can be compared in the same frame of reference. Correlation techniques, regression lines, linear and nonlinear discriminants are discussed so that the proper choice of the technique to be employed in a practical problem can be facilitated. Since input information is not always numerical but is sometimes the result of subjective value judgment, methods of assigning numerical values to nonnumerical input data is discussed. Two practical illustrations are given.

5.1 GEOMETRICAL INTERPRETATION OF CLASSIFICATION PROCEDURES

In the foregoing discussions a number of different procedures were discussed for learning the recognition of class membership from samples of given classes. Discriminant functions, estimates of probability densities, and various linear and nonlinear transformations were derived for finding boundaries of the N-space that optimally enclose members of a class and that separate, with a minimum of error, those of another. Differences in the procedures arose partly from differences in the manner in which the classification problem of pattern recognition was stated mathematically and partly from differences in the constraints imposed on the permissible solutions. Since the various methods developed in the different chapters have different properties, one may wonder which should be employed in seeking a solution to a given practical problem. Although the likelihood ratio computation or its approximation is always the best solution, for reasons of limited storage facility it is sometimes economically prohibitive to employ. If a clear understanding of the capabilities and limitations of the learning procedures is gained, it is often possible to make a practical choice of methods consistent with the allowable complexities and other constraints of the required solution. The purpose of the present discussion is to impart to the reader an appreciation of some of the subtleties of the learning procedures through a geometrical interpretation of their capabilities and limitations. To complete the discussion of decision procedures, several often used methods not treated thus far will also be discussed. Among these, correlation methods are most prominent.

Correlation with Stored References

An often used procedure in decision making and thus in pattern recogni-
is to correlate the input vector to be classified with each of several
stored references that represent the different classes to which the input
may belong. Among others, the recognition of printed characters in type-
readers and that of sounds in sound-recognizers has been attempted in
this way. The stored references are often the means of the set of samples
of the different classes. Decisions are made by comparing the correlation
between the input and each of the stored references and by deciding that
the input is a member of the class corresponding to the largest correlation
coefficient. The capabilities and shortcomings of this decision rule are
best illustrated by considering the relationship between two classes and
the type of decision regions that may be obtained. Since correlation com-
putes a dot product, it is a measurement of the cosine of the angle between the reference and the input, x. If a is the angle between m_A and x,
β the angle between m_B and x, the boundary between the region where x
is classed in A and that where it is classified as a member of B is a
straight line that passes through the origin and causes $|m_B| \cos \beta =
|m_A| \cos a$. This is illustrated in the two-dimensional example of Fig.
5-1. No matter what relationship m_B may bear to members of the class B,
it is easy to envision practical situations in which members of B lie in
the region in which inputs are classified as belonging to A. A typical
situation of this sort is depicted in the figure where a subset of points
belonging to A lie in the region where they would be classed in B.

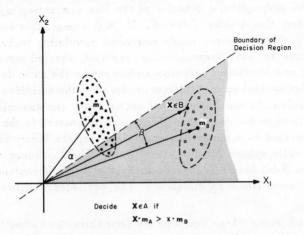

Figure 5-1. Decisions by maximum correlation.

A special case of frequent occurrence is that where $|m_A| = |m_B|$. This occurs particularly often in communications problems where m_A and m_B represent specific signal waveforms immersed in noise. The vector x is the noisy observation of either m_A or m_B and the decision maker attempts to decide, upon observing x, whether m_A or m_B was transmitted. If m_A and m_B are normalized, by equating their magnitudes, the decision region boundary is the bisector of the angle between the two points m_A and m_B. Thus correlation decisions are based on the angular proximity between input and reference signals. It is a useful method of making decisions if the angular spread between members of a class is small compared to the angular separation between classes.

Another special case of practical interest is that where all inputs are constrained to have equal magnitudes. Signals passing through amplifiers with automatic gain controls, photographic images of fixed average density, and black-and-white characters of equal black area are among those inputs that possess vector representations of equal magnitude in the most often employed vector spaces. Since vectors must now always lie on a sphere, they can differ from one another only in the direction and in the magnitude of the angular deviation from the stored references.

Euclidean Distance from Stored References

Another method of making classification decisions is based on a comparison of the Euclidean distance between the input x and the stored references m_A and m_B. The decision rule that emerges from a comparison of Euclidean distances states that $x \in A$ if $|x - m_A| < |x - m_B|$. This rule partitions the space into two regions A and B by a single straight line. The perpendicular bisector of the line connecting m_A and m_B is the boundary that divides A from B. If $|m_A| = |m_B|$, this boundary coincides with that of the previously described correlation technique. Since this is true in many communication systems, squared error (Euclidean distance) and correlation techniques often render the same decisions.

Another special case of interest occurs when the variables of the multivariate process or multidimensional vector space can assume only binary values. Such is the case when figures and characters in the visual field are represented by a binary sequence signifying the binary intensities of a set of cells scanned in the visual field. The Euclidean distance between two N-bit binary sequences thought of as N-dimensional vectors is the well-known Hamming distance.* The equivalence between Hamming

*Hamming, R. W. "Error Detecting and Error Correcting Codes," Bell System Tech. J., 1950.

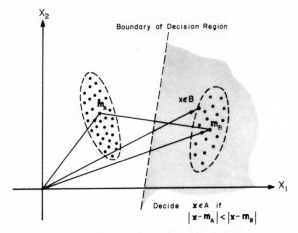

Figure 5-2. Comparison of Euclidean distances.

distance and Euclidean distance is almost complete and extends to the equivalence relationship established above between decisions based on smallest Euclidean distance and largest correlation coefficient.

We should note, however, that while decisions based on maximum correlation and minimum Euclidean distance are very similar, particularly in the important special cases we discussed, this similarity ceases when thresholds are used to avoid decision making in uncertain cases. Suppose, for instance, that, if the correlation between input and reference is less than a suitable threshold value, we would not consider the decision trustworthy and would like to refrain from making decisions. A similar demand may be made of decisions employing distance measurements. If the distance between input and any of the means of the classes exceeds a threshold value, we would reject any decision on the grounds that the input is not "close" enough to either one of the classes. While decisions without the use of thresholds are similar, the thresholded decision regions exhibit the fundamentally different nature of angle-sensitive correlation and the Euclidean metric. In Fig. 5-3 the decision regions that result when the thresholded Euclidean distance is used in classification are indicated by the vertically shaded region, while those which result from correlation are shown shaded horizontally. The line l is the common decision region boundary without the use of thresholds.

Regression Lines and Curves

The scatter diagram illustrated in Fig. 5-4 is a portrayal of the set of given samples of a class A in two dimensions. The machine that learns

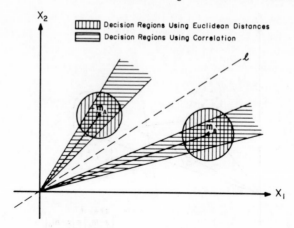

Figure 5-3. The use of thresholds.

how membership in this class is to be determined tries to extract a definition of the class in terms of its characteristics. If the language of characteristics with which the machine is endowed is restricted to the expression of simple linear relationships between variables, one might describe the class by saying that its samples lie more or less on a straight line. The linear mean-square regression line which passes through the mean of the set of points with a slope proportional to the correlation between variables is the "best" such line. A measure of membership in

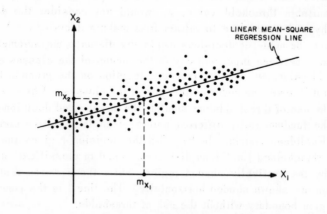

Figure 5-4. Linear mean-square regression line.

the class is sometimes taken to correspond to how close the point in question is to the regression line. If there are two or more classes, and they are each characterized by their linear mean-square regression lines, we might decide that a point to be classified belongs to the class whose

regression line is closest to the point in question. The resultant decision
regions are shown in Fig. 5-5. The boundaries between decision regions
are the bisectors of the angles between regression lines. The space is
thus divided into quadrants. A simplified implementation of decisions
based on proximity of a point to the nearest regression line can be achieved

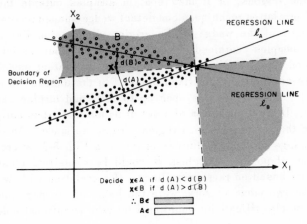

**Figure 5-5. Classification based on proximity to
nearest regression line.**

by a translation of the origin of the coordinate system to $0'$, the point of
intersection of the regression lines. Recalling the properties of decisions
based on correlation, we see that closeness to the nearest regression line
is implemented by a comparison of the correlation between the input, in

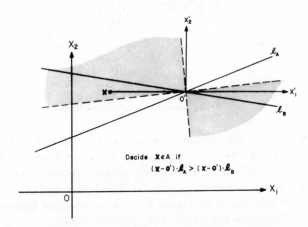

**Figure 5-6. Computational simplification of clas-
sification by translation of origin and
correlation.**

the translated coordinate system, and unit vectors in the direction of the regression lines.

In all the decision procedures discussed thus far, it is obvious that serious errors will be made if the class to be recognized has members that are distributed in a manner fundamentally different from the shape of the decision regions, or if they contain samples outside the decision regions. Correlation techniques can detect wedge-shaped scatter diagrams with the apex of the wedge at the origin. Regression line techniques can detect samples contained in wedges centered about the intersections of regression lines, and Euclidean distances can detect samples falling into circles concentric about fixed points. In the absence of restraining thresholds, wedge angles can open up to 180° and circles can have infinite radii. If the distribution of a set of points has a basically different shape from that of the decision region, errors are made. An illustration of shortcomings of such limitations is given in Fig. 5-7, where a significant portion of points from class *B* would be classified class *A* if decisions were based on regression lines. If correlation with two vectors, such as the two mean vectors, were the basis of the decision rule, the number of misclassifications would still be very significant indeed.

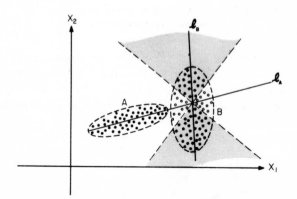

Figure 5-7. Illustration of shortcoming of decisions based on regression lines.

There is no particular reason, however, why we should insist on passing the best straight line through points in a scatter diagram. At the expense of more complicated equipment, greater storage, and increased computation time, a better curve can be fitted to a set of points. The curve may be a polynomial of degree K, or a generalized harmonic series of K terms, to illustrate but a few of the possibilities.

The best fitting curve (least squares fit) passing through a set of points can be obtained simply. It will be derived for a two-dimensional case below. The squared error between given samples and the best fitting curve is given in Eq. (5.1), where a_k is the kth unknown coefficient of combination of the functions $\phi_k(x)$ that compose the curve, and x_{1m}, x_{2m} are the coordinates of the mth sample point.

$$E = \sum_{m=1}^{M} \left[x_{2m} - \sum_{k=0}^{K} a_k \phi_k(x_{1m}) \right]^2 . \tag{5.1}$$

Differentiation of the error with respect to the unknown coefficients of combination is the first step in solving for a_k. The rest of the steps follow the usual methods of the calculus of variations.

$$\frac{\partial E}{\partial a_s} = 0 = \frac{1}{M} \sum_{m=1}^{M} x_{2m} \phi_s(x_{1m}) -$$

$$- \frac{1}{M} \sum_{m=1}^{M} \sum_{k=0}^{K} a_k \phi_k(x_{1m}) \phi_s(x_{1m}) \qquad \text{for } s = 0, 1, \ldots, K. \tag{5.2a}$$

$$\overline{x_2 \phi_s(x_1)} = \sum_{k=0}^{K} a_k \overline{\phi_k(x_1) \phi_s(x_1)} \qquad \text{for } s = 0, 1, \ldots, K. \tag{5.2b}$$

By letting $\overline{x_s \phi_s(x_1)} = b_s$ and $\overline{\phi_k(x_1) \phi_s(x_1)} = \gamma_{ks}$, we can rewrite the above as a matrix equation and solve it for $\mathbf{a}$, the vector composed of the a_k coordinates.

$$\mathbf{a} = \mathbf{b} \gamma^{-1}. \tag{5.3}$$

In Eq. (5.3), γ is the matrix composed of elements γ_{ks} and $\mathbf{b}$ is the vector composed of elements b_s.

It is interesting to note that if the set of functions $\phi_k(x_1) = x_1{}^k$; that is, if we fit a polynomial to the set of points, and if the degree of the polynomial is restricted to one (straight line fitting), we obtain the linear regression line once more.

In conformity with previously discussed decision procedures using regression lines, one may examine the x_1 coordinate of a given point to be classified to see if the x_2 coordinate lies closer to the regression curve of class A or to that of class B, evaluated at x_1. The decision boundary is thus the algebraic mean of the two regression curves. This is shown in Fig. 5-8. The dotted curve shows a line that bisects the shortest distance between the two regression curves. This latter, aside from difficulties of implementation, is a more appealing decision boundary than the algebraic mean.

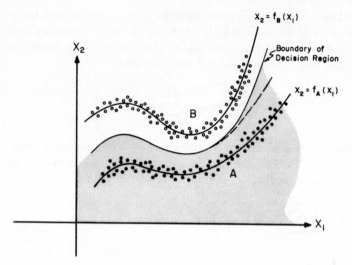

Figure 5-8. Mean-square regression curves

Decide $\mathbf{x} \epsilon A$, if

$$x_2 - \sum_{k=0}^{K} \frac{1}{2}(a_{ak} - a_{bk})x_1 > 0,$$

where a_{ak} and a_{bk} are the constants a_k found from classes A and B, respectively.

As the number of dimensions of the space increases, the regression curves become surfaces. Although regression curves in N dimensions are not very useful in making classification decisions, the notion of a surface in the N-space will be useful when dealing with discriminant functions. A regression surface of x_3 versus x_1 and x_2 is illustrated in Fig. 5-9. In this figure, sections of constant x_3 can be regarded as a family of regression curves where x_3 selects which member of the family is applicable.

Linear Transformations and Discriminants

Linear discriminants in the N-space are straight lines along which members of a class are clustered while classes are separated from one another. The various discriminants of Chapter II differ from each other in the particular properties of classes by which an attempt is made to separate classes and gather together samples within a class. As a re-

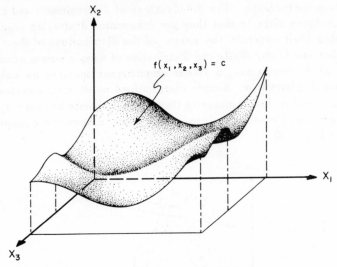

Figure 5-9. Regression curve in N dimensions.

sult of these differences, the direction in the N-space in which the discriminants are pointing differ somewhat. A qualitative description of the geometrical significance of these differences is given below.

The mathematical problems that lead to the derivation of a discriminant are generally stated as minimization or maximization problems with suitable constraints to keep constant certain inter or intra-class properties. Minimization problems desire to reduce intra-class distances while keeping some inter-class distances constant. The constant constraints may keep the distance between means, the mean-square interset, or the average total of inter and intraset distances constant. The maximization problems desire to separate different classes by some interset properties while keeping members within the same class together by virtue of holding constant certain intraset properties. Various problems attempt to maximize the distance between means or the mean-square interset distance while holding intraset distances constant. Certain equivalences between the maximization and minimization problems can be shown. For instance, minimization of the mean-square intraset distance while holding the distance between the means of two classes constant is equivalent to the maximization of the distance between means while holding the mean-square intraset distance constant. Other equivalences are equally evident.

The advantage of discriminant techniques of classification is their simplicity. A discriminant is a linear combination of the coordinates of the space in N dimensions. Thinking of the discriminant as a unit vector, classification by discriminants is a comparison of dot products or

correlation coefficients. The disadvantage of discriminants and correlation techniques alike is that they are information destroying processes.
They also limit severely the nature of the distributions of the classes
which they can learn. While the distribution of sample points occupies a
volume of N dimensions, a linear discriminant operates on only one-
dimensional information. Sample distributions in all other directions are
ignored. Another disadvantage of linear discriminants becomes apparent
as the number of classes is increased. A few illustrative examples are
shown in Fig. 5-10.

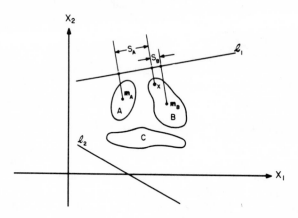

Figure 5-10. Linear discriminant.

The regions enclosed by the closed contours indicate the regions in
which most of the members of the class in question are contained. The
normal function of the discriminant (the direction of line ℓ_1) is to separate members of A and B and render decisions with few errors between A
and B. A typical decision rule is given below. This is also illustrated
in Fig. 5-10.

$$\text{Decide } \mathbf{x} \in A, \text{ if } S_A = |\ell_1 \cdot (\mathbf{x} - \mathbf{m}_A)| < S_B = |\ell_1 \cdot (\mathbf{x} - \mathbf{m}_B)|. \qquad (5.4)$$

The line ℓ_1 indeed has the property that every $\mathbf{x}$ contained in A or B is
correctly classified by the above decision rule. If the additional class C
is introduced, however, no direction in the two-dimensional space can be
found that separates A from B and C by means of a single linear discriminant. Projections of some points in C will always be mistaken for
members of A, even if another discriminant ℓ_2 is chosen. This latter discriminant was chosen to separate A from the union of B and C. If a different discriminant is developed for each pair of classes, as shown in
Fig. 5-11, the space may still be divided into decision regions that contain only members of one class. In Fig. 5-11 the line labeled ℓ_{AB} is intended to distinguish members of A from B; ℓ_{BC} and ℓ_{AC} are likewise
intended to distinguish B from C and A from C, respectively.

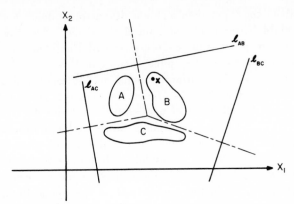

Figure 5-11. Use of multiple discriminants.

In the classification of the point x, first the projection of x onto, let us say, ℓ_{AC} is compared with the projections of the means of A and C onto the same line. Since the projection of x is closer to that of the mean of A than to that of C, we would decide, by the above-stated decision rule, that x is more likely a member of A than C. This tentative decision assumes, according to the manner in which discriminants are employed in decision making, that only the binary choice of membership in A or C is available. We would now compare membership in A (the winner of the previous contest) and B by use of ℓ_{AB}. We would find that B is a more likely choice than A and would thus have made a correct decision. Had the first contest between A and C, gone in favor of C, the next comparison, that between B and C, would still have resulted in the correct decision of classifying x as a member of B. It is apparent from the geometry that this method of making decisions results in the correct recognition of class membership whenever the regions A, B, C are convex. It is readily appreciated from the geometrical picture that if A, B, and C occupy regions that are not convex or not simply connected, linear discriminants, or linear methods of any kind for that matter, will not provide adequate discrimination between classes.

The linear transformation that minimizes the mean-square distance between members of the same class without regard to the distribution of members of other classes is, in general, a more powerful tool in decision making. It was pointed out in Chapter II that the measurement of distance after a linear transformation of the vector space is equivalent to using ellipsoidal equidistance contours in a distance-comparing decision rule. The resulting contours are also contours of equiprobable membership in the Gaussian N-variate process that best fits the given set of samples. It should be noted that decisions based on linear transformations of the vector space retain information about the distribution of the samples in N mutually orthogonal directions. It thus preserves more information about the input than a linear discriminant does; hence it is expected to yield better decisions, on the average. We proved that, assuming Gaussian processes, a comparison of Euclidean distances after linear transformations of the space results in Bayes' decisions. Since decisions based on linear discriminants are different and are thus not Bayes' decisions; decisions by linear discriminants must yield a higher probability of error and must of necessity be inferior decision rules. If the two classes have equal covariance matrices, linear discriminants and fitting Gaussian probability densities to the set of given points yield identical decisions. There are subtle differences that exist, however, between the two methods even in the case of equal covariance matrices. These differences, as in the comparison of Euclidean distances versus linear mean-square regression lines, exhibit themselves when a threshold is employed in rejecting untrustworthy decisions. Following the line of reasoning employed previously, the reader can readily compare the thresholded decision regions that result when discriminants are employed with the ellipsoidal regions that result from fitting Gaussian densities to the given samples. In general, the linear transformations yield good classification decisions in practical problems where there is reason to believe that the probability densities of classes are unimodal; i.e., they possess only a single hump.

There are significant computational differences between linear discriminants and the fitting of Gaussian probability densities to a set of samples. With the latter method K quadratic forms must be evaluated, where K is the number of classes. Each quadratic form in N dimensions is computed from N dot products. In comparison to computing dot products, the other operations involved in the calculation of a quadratic form are not significant. Thus NK dot products must be computed, and storage must be provided for an equal number of N-dimensional vectors. If linear discriminants are employed, however, storage must be provided for as many N-dimensional vectors as there are pairs of classes. If there are K classes, $K(K-1)/2$, discriminants must be available for computation. Thus if the inequality given in Eq. (5.5) holds, the computation of the theoretically superior method of evaluating Gaussian probability densities is, from a storage point of view, also more economical.

$$N < (K-1)/2. \tag{5.5}$$

It should be noted that only $K-1$ discriminants need be computed to make a decision among K possible classes. Which $K-1$ of the $K(K-1)/2$ should be computed, however, becomes evident only as the sequence of computations progresses. In the two-dimensional, three-class situation illustrated in Fig. 5-11, for instance, only ℓ_{AC} and ℓ_{AB} were used to make decisions but ℓ_{BC} also had to be available, had the first decision gone in favor of class C.

The geometrical interpretation of two of the often occurring mathematical quantities will now be given. In the application of linear discriminants, as well as in fitting Gaussian probability densities to a set of samples of a class, eigenvalues and eigenvectors of covariance matrices are frequently occurring quantities. The geometrical significance of these quantities can be interpreted directly. The eigenvector of the discriminant problem is the discriminant itself. It is the direction of the N-space in which classes are most separable. The corresponding eigenvalue usually denotes the magnitude of the quantity that is maximized or minimized in the solution of the linear discriminant problem. In fitting Gaussian probability densities to a set of samples of a class, eigenvectors of the covariance matrices indicate the directions in the N-space in which diameters of the best fitting ellipsoid lie. Eigenvalues are the squares of the semimajor axes and they also express the variance of the set of points in the direction of the corresponding eigenvectors. The smallest eigenvalue, therefore, is a measure of the variance of the samples in the direction in which this variance is a minimum. The corresponding eigenvector expresses the "property" most invariant from sample to sample within the class in question. It is thus the most invariant property of the class.

It will be recalled that the square of the determinant of the covariance matrix of a set of vectors is the product of eigenvalues of the covariance matrix. By virtue of the above geometrical interpretation of eigenvalues, a singular covariance matrix implies that the magnitude of at least one of the diameters of the best fitting ellipsoid is zero. It is readily seen that this will always be the case if the number of sample points is equal to or less than the number of dimensions of the space. In two dimensions, for example, two or less points are always colinear. The best fitting ellipse has therefore zero dimensions in a direction orthogonal to the line connecting the pair of points. This is the geometrical reason why the minimum number of sample points to which an N-variate Gaussian probability density can be fitted must exceed the number of dimensions of the vector space. This fact can become quite objectionable in practice when we are often forced to deal with very high-dimensional spaces and the number of available samples is limited.

Generalized Discriminants and Nonlinear Methods

The inherent limitations of linear methods of classificatory analysis are their inability to find better fits to the arbitrary distribution of given samples of a class than the spherical, ellipsoidal, or planar shapes already discussed. As a result, the simple situation in which a class consists of two disjointed subclasses cannot be handled, in general, by linear methods. The nonlinear generalized discriminant analysis technique of Chapter III is required to overcome this limitation. This technique is one which assumes that a discriminant function exists in the form of a function of the N-space (a surface in $N+1$ dimensions) and that samples of different classes along the discriminant — the height of the $N+1$ dimensional surface — occupy disjointed intervals. Classes are thus separable. It is readily appreciated from Fig. 5-12 that, since the height of the surface over any point in the N-space is arbitrary, the surface can be arranged to have the same height over any member of class A. Similarly, the surface may be made to have a different but

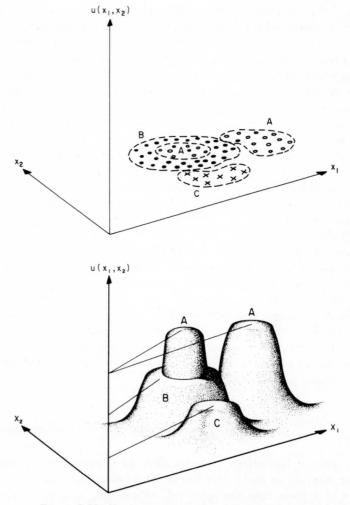

Figure 5-12. Nonlinear discriminant of three classes.

linear methods. The nonlinear generalized discriminant analysis technique of Chapter III is required to overcome this limitation. This technique is one which assumes that a discriminant function exists in the form of a function of the N-space (a surface in $N + 1$ dimensions) and that samples of different classes along the discriminant — the height of the $N + 1$ dimensional surface — occupy disjointed intervals. Classes are thus separable. It is readily appreciated from Fig. 5-12 that, since the height of the surface over any point in the N-space is arbitrary, the surface can be arranged to have the same height over any member of class A. Similarly, the surface may be made to have a different but

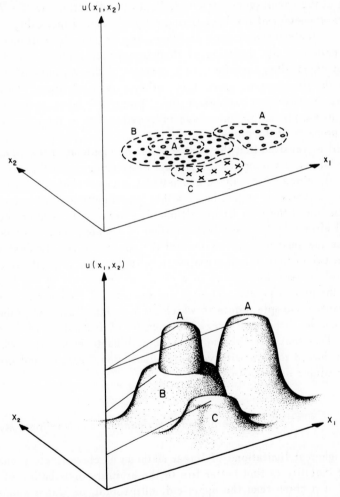

Figure 5-12. Nonlinear discriminant of three classes.

The geometrical interpretation of two of the often occurring mathematical quantities will now be given. In the application of linear discriminants, as well as in fitting Gaussian probability densities to a set of samples of a class, eigenvalues and eigenvectors of covariance matrices are frequently occurring quantities. The geometrical significance of these quantities can be interpreted directly. The eigenvector of the discriminant problem is the discriminant itself. It is the direction of the N-space in which classes are most separable. The corresponding eigenvalue usually denotes the magnitude of the quantity that is maximized or minimized in the solution of the linear discriminant problem. In fitting Gaussian probability densities to a set of samples of a class, eigenvectors of the covariance matrices indicate the directions in the N-space in which diameters of the best fitting ellipsoid lie. Eigenvalues are the squares of the semimajor axes and they also express the variance of the set of points in the direction of the corresponding eigenvectors. The smallest eigenvalue, therefore, is a measure of the variance of the samples in the direction in which this variance is a minimum. The corresponding eigenvector expresses the "property" most invariant from sample to sample within the class in question. It is thus the most invariant property of the class.

It will be recalled that the square of the determinant of the covariance matrix of a set of vectors is the product of eigenvalues of the covariance matrix. By virtue of the above geometrical interpretation of eigenvalues, a singular covariance matrix implies that the magnitude of at least one of the diameters of the best fitting ellipsoid is zero. It is readily seen that this will always be the case if the number of sample points is equal to or less than the number of dimensions of the space. In two dimensions, for example, two or less points are always colinear. The best fitting ellipse has therefore zero dimensions in a direction orthogonal to the line connecting the pair of points. This is the geometrical reason why the minimum number of sample points to which an N-variate Gaussian probability density can be fitted must exceed the number of dimensions of the vector space. This fact can become quite objectionable in practice when we are often forced to deal with very high-dimensional spaces and the number of available samples is limited.

Generalized Discriminants and Nonlinear Methods

The inherent limitations of linear methods of classificatory analysis are their inability to find better fits to the arbitrary distribution of given samples of a class than the spherical, ellipsoidal, or planar shapes already discussed. As a result, the simple situation in which a class consists of two disjointed subclasses cannot be handled, in general, by equal value over all samples of class B. Only the permissible complexities of the surface limit the generality of the distribution of given samples. If, for instance, the surface is restricted to a Kth degree polynomial in N dimensions, the number of points of local extreme the surface may have is usually limited to substantially less than K. The geometrical representation of nonlinear discriminants also makes it clear that, at least in principle, discriminants can be applied to the separation of members of an arbitrary number of classes.

In order to achieve this objective, it is necessary only to construct a surface that has as many levels as there are classes to be separated from one another. Figure 5-12 shows the separation of three classes, where A consists of two subclasses. B is an annulus surrounding one of the subclasses of A, and C is a fairly isolated region. Recognition consists of the evaluation of the discriminant — the evaluation of the height of the surface — and a comparison of the value thus obtained with each of the three values that the discriminant can have. In practice, however, the number of coefficients that must be determined in finding a suitable approximation of the nonlinear function becomes very large as the number of classes, dimensions of the space, and degree of the approximating function are raised. The matrix that must be inverted to find the optimum choice of unknown coefficients becomes prohibitively large. It is for this reason that less sophisticated methods must often be employed to solve practical problems.

If there is reason to believe that a group of variables is statistically independent from another group of variables, the probability density can be factored into the product of the joint densities of the groups. Assume, for instance, that we have a six-dimensional space in which the first three variables are independent of the second set of three variables even though, within each group, variables are interdependent. We can apply the nonlinear techniques to each of the two groups of three variables, obtaining thus two discriminant functions $u_1(x_1, x_2, x_3)$, and $u_2(x_4, x_5, x_6)$. Each six-dimensional vector of the $x_1 \cdots x_6$ space can now be represented as a two-dimensional vector in the u_1, u_2 space of discriminant functions. A new discriminant $u_3(u_1, u_2)$ can now be found by the same procedure that yielded u_1 and u_2. This procedure results in no loss of generality as long as the groups of variables on which the discriminants are found are indeed statistically independent. The procedure described above is not applicable in general. Unfortunately, there are no tests that can be performed to measure the degree of statistical dependence of groups of variables, except if it is known that the variables are jointly Gaussianly distributed. It is precisely in this special case, however, that we have the least use for a test of this sort, since substantially no difficulty is encountered in fitting joint Gaussian processes to data in almost any number of dimensions. The practical implementation of the method for finding optimum nonlinear discriminants remains one of the problems yet to be solved. In many physical problems where the number of dimensions of the space are few and there is reason to believe that the probability densities of the classes, although not unimodal, are reasonably "well-behaved," nonlinear discriminants can be successfully employed. The recognition of specific vowel sounds from "formant" frequencies is a typical illustrative example of such a problem. In the three or four-dimensional space of formant frequencies, samples of a vowel sound uttered by males and females form two fairly tight clusters separated from one another.

5.2 ASSIGNMENT OF NUMERICAL VALUES TO SUBJECTIVE MEASUREMENTS

In many practical problems the dimensions of the vector space do not always represent quantitatively measurable properties. Subjective value judgments, yes-no decisions, and quantized judgments (small, medium, and high) are often encountered inputs to a man-machine decision environment. Yet, processing of data obtained in this way must still be accomplished by numerical methods. It is important to consider, therefore, the influence of numerical value assignment of subjective measurements on the success or failure of the classification techniques discussed earlier. It is clear, of course, that the assignment of numerical values to subjective measurements in no way influences the decision procedure of Chapters III and IV, since nonlinear transformations and the sample selecting techniques can form the boundaries of arbitrary distributions of input samples. Correlation, linear discriminant, and Gaussian process fitting techniques, however, are usually very sensitive to the method of assigning coordinate values (but not to changes of scale factors) since these can handle only limited distributions of inputs.

If the dimension of the space in which coordinate value assignment is desired has physical significance in terms of the problem to be solved, then logically adjacent coordinate values (good, fair, poor) may be assigned adjacent numerical values. Often, however, we do not know whether to assign 1, 2, 3 to good, fair, and poor, respectively, or whether a different set of numerical values might result in a better distribution of samples in the vector space. Since simplicity of the decision procedure is always to be desired, coordinate value assignment of subjective measurements can be made so that the distribution of the sample measurement values be Gaussian. This is desirable since the simplest linear techniques best separate joint Gaussian densities. If samples of two or more classes are available, coordinate value assignments should be made so that maximum separation between members of different classes should be maintained. These two aspects of the problem will be described below.

In both cases we may start by assigning *arbitrary* numerical values to the scale of subjective judgment x. Thus the probability density of observing the numerical value x from members of a given class and given dimension is $p(x)$. We now wish to find the permanent coordinate value assignment by considering the reassignment of numerical values to the initial arbitrary coordinate values x. We thus look for a function $y(x)$ so that $y(x)$ is Gaussianly distributed. This can be illustrated in Fig. 5-13, where x is the arbitrary assignment, the points on x are the observed samples, and $y(x)$ maps x into y so that mappings of samples of x on y are Gaussianly distributed.

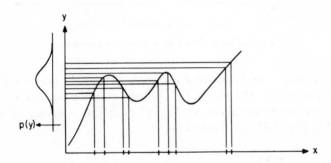

Figure 5-13. Transformation of an arbitrary random variable to a Gaussian variable.

We will now show that a function $y(x)$ of the random variable x exists that will render y a Gaussian random variable. The only restriction requires that the density $p(x)$ be piecewise continuous. The transformation $y(x)$ is therefore a "Gaussianizing" transformation.

If $p(x)$ is the probability density of the variable x, then $P(x)$, given by Eq. (5.6), is the cumulative distribution function.

$$P(x) = P(\xi < x) = \int_{-\infty}^{x} p(\xi) \, d\xi. \tag{5.6}$$

Let us assume that $P(x)$ is continuous. This is assured if $p(x)$ is piecewise continuous (contains no discontinuities of higher order than steps).

Consider $P(x)$ to be a function of x. Since x is a random variable, $P(x)$, a function of x, is also a random variable. The interesting property of $P(x)$ as a random variable is that it is uniformly distributed between 0 and 1. Instead of giving a rigorous proof of this statement, we can illustrate this fact by noting, as shown in Fig. 5-14, that $P(x)$ increases by $1/M$ at each of the M samples of the variable x. Samples of x are mapped uniformly into $z = P(x)$.

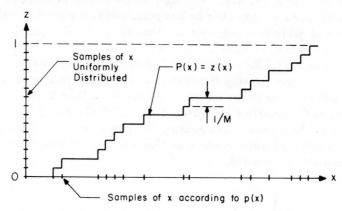

Figure 5-14. *$P(x)$ as a mapping function.*

The variable z is distributed uniformly; $p(z) = 1$, between 0 and 1, $p(z) = 0$ elsewhere. We would like to map z into y so that y is Gaussianly distributed, as given in Eq. (5.7). The mapping of $y(z)$ is sketched in Fig. 5-15 and derived below.

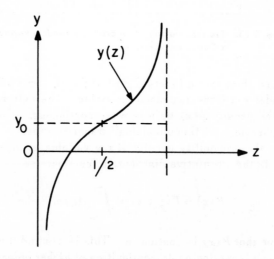

Figure 5-15. *Mapping Z into a Gaussian variable.*

$$p(y) = \frac{1}{\sqrt{2\pi}\,\sigma} \exp\left(-\frac{(y - y_0)^2}{2\sigma^2}\right). \tag{5.7}$$

For simplicity, define the new variable $y_1 = (y - y_0)/\sigma$ and find the mapping $y_1(z)$, sketched below. $p(y_1)$ is given in Eq. (5.8).

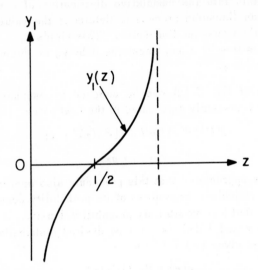

Figure 5-16. Mapping Z into a Gaussian variable.

$$p(y_1) = \frac{1}{\sqrt{2\pi}\,\sigma}\, \exp\left(-\frac{1}{2}y_1^2\right). \tag{5.8}$$

The cumulative probability distribution $P(y < y_1) = P[z < z(y_1)]$.

$$P(y < y_1) = \frac{1}{\sqrt{2\pi}} \int_{-\infty}^{y_1} \exp\left[-\frac{1}{2}y^2\right] dy =$$

$$= \int_0^{z(y_1)} p(z)\, dz = z(y_1); \qquad \text{since } p(z) = 1. \tag{5.9}$$

Hence

$$z = \frac{1}{\sqrt{2\pi}} \int_{-\infty}^{y_1} \exp\left[-\frac{1}{2}y_1^2\right] dy_1 = P_0(y_1); \tag{5.10}$$

$$y_1 = P_0^{-1}(z) = P_0^{-1}[P(x)]; \tag{5.11}$$

$$y = y_0 + \sigma P_0^{-1}[P(x)], \tag{5.12}$$

where P_0 is given by Eq. (5.10) and $P(x)$ by Eq. (5.6).

Operationally, therefore, the transformation that Gaussianly distributes the transformed variable of density $p(x)$ is the mapping that:

a. Looks up the cumulative distribution function's value at the point x, $P(x)$.

b. Enters this into the cumulative distribution of a unit variance, zero mean Gaussian process to determine the value of the argument of the Gaussian distribution. This yields y_1.

c. Multiplies this by σ and translates it by y_0 to obtain the new random variable y.

The result of Eq. (5.12) can be checked by assuming that x was normalized and Gaussianly distributed in the first place. Hence

$$P_0^{-1}[P(x)] = P_0^{-1}[P_0(x)] = x; \qquad (5.13a)$$

$$y = y_0 + \sigma x. \qquad (5.13b)$$

It is readily appreciated that this procedure also applies to the conversion of the variable x, regardless of its probability density, to a random variable y that has an arbitrary probability density. If $P_1(x)$ is the distribution of x and $P_0(y)$ is the new desired distribution, the transformation $y(x)$ is given by Eq. (5.14).

$$y(x) = P_0^{-1}[P_1(x)]. \qquad (5.14)$$

If samples of two or more classes are given, we can still start with the arbitrary coordinate value assignment x. We now look for the mapping $u(x)$ that maximally separates members of one class from those of another. This function was derived in Chapter III. Nonlinear discriminants can thus be used to assign numerical values to subjective measurements. In Fig. 5-17, for instance, the function $u(x)$ separates the two kinds of samples marked x and 0 and thus specifies the change of coordinate value assignment. With this transformation members of different classes can be separated from one another along the original coordinate axes. This process does not guarantee, however, that the *joint* densities of the classes are simpler functions.

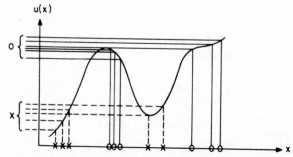

Figure 5-17. *Reassignment of coordinate values by use of nonlinear discriminants.*

5.3 SELECTION OF A COMPUTATIONAL PROCEDURE

The choice of computational procedure best suited to a specific problem is influenced by two different problems of practical interest. One of these is the problem where, by reasons beyond our control, we are constrained to accept a given vector representation of the physical world. The other is one where the dimensions of the vector space and the number of such dimensions is within our power to choose.

An example of the former is the problem where we wish to decide, from a sequence of N throws of a die, whether the die is biased (loaded) or not. Here the choice of dimensions is already essentially firm. The dimensions of the vector space must be the different instances of casting the die (first throw, second throw, . . . , N^{th} throw), and the coordinate values are the numbers, 1 through 6, that are turned face up on a particular throw of the die. The vector representation of a throw sequence is the set of N numbers that indicate the numerical values of the sides of the die that are found face up in the sequence of N throws.

In other problems the choice of dimensions and the number to choose are not clear cut. This is the situation that exists, for instance, in the recognition of types of objects. The number of different attributes of objects we must describe in order to gain a complete characterization of the object is beyond the capabilities of any machine. Therefore choices of descriptors or lists of properties must be generated that will, for the purposes of discrimination between a finite number of object types, sufficiently well represent all objects. This choice, in most instances, is difficult and can be made only intuitively.

In other instances, as in the case of the recognition of speech events, there is at least one method of representation that is sufficient to preserve all needed information; it may be too complicated, however, to be used directly. A spoken word, for instance, can be represented by means of the output waveform of a microphone into which the word is spoken. Even if we assume that speech is band limited at 4000 cps, it would take an approximately 8000-dimensional space to represent one second of speech. The choice of dimensions also plays a prominent role. Samples taken at the Nyquist rate and expansion in a Fourier series are among suitable representations of waveforms. Yet in the two vector spaces constructed from sample heights and Fourier coefficients, the same set of waveforms have entirely different probability densities. The choice of representation is ours to make and is governed only by estimates of the complexity of the task of recognition and of the task of implementing the implied measurements.

Often the choice of dimensions of the vector space are made by postulating "potentially useful" descriptors of the classes which we wish to separate. Descriptors, when thought of by humans, tend to lead to fairly simple distributions of classes in the resulting vector space. This is because when we describe a class of objects we tend to describe them in terms of their common properties. Common properties are those which have substantially the same value in all members of a class.

Once the dimensions of the space are chosen, a number of representative samples of the class must be selected. The exact number of samples is not significant, although different methods of data processing discussed in preceding chapters are influenced to a different extent by the sample size on which they operate. Estimates of the required sample size can be made by statistical methods (in some cases); here, however, only practical, "rule of thumb," estimates will be discussed.

Generally speaking, the number of samples required by decision procedures is related to the number of undetermined coefficients that must be established by the learning process. Linear discriminant and correlation techniques require the smallest number of given samples, since only first or, sometimes, second order statistics are needed to establish the decision rules. Decision rules that use various distance measures discussed in Chapter II, must estimate covariance matrices with a corresponding increase of the required sample size. Samples should number in excess of the number of dimensions of the space. There are ways of avoiding this requirement in practice. From a mathematical point of of view, a sample size several times the number of dimensions of the space is desirable. In the illustration of spoken numeral recognition this requirement could not be met, yet excellent results were achieved.

In using the nonlinear methods of Chapter III, a fairly large number of samples are required, since the method employs estimates of higher moments of the probability densities. The number of samples on which recognition is learned should exceed $\binom{N + p}{p}$, a binomial coefficient that depends on N, the number of dimensions, and p the degree of the polynomial.

The adaptive methods of Chapter IV require only enough samples to act as representative samples of a class. This is always a minimal requirement that must be met if any technique is to yield satisfactory performance.

After the selection of the vector space and the samples, the method of computation to be employed must be chosen. In the solution of practical physical problems this choice can be made relatively easily, for physical arguments can often be advanced in support of the adequacy of one procedure or another. The simplest solution is always the most desirable one, since it is usually the one that can be implemented most readily. Experimental evidence may indicate that members of a class lie close to one another and classes are well separated. If this is the case, linear discriminants or, at any rate, the method of employing linear transformations to cluster members of classes will, in general, result in decision making with a sufficiently low error probability.

If classes are believed to consist of subclasses, groups that are believed to possess different properties, it is best not to consider the employment of *any* of the linear methods (methods that use linear transformations or linear combinations). If the number of dimensions is low, nonlinear methods discussed in Chapter III are promising. Even if storage limitations would prevent their direct employment, several uses (i.e., iterative use) of nonlinear methods would still provide useful results. Nonlinear discriminants of subgroups of the variables can be found, and an input vector can be represented as the set of numerical values of discriminants of the subgroups evaluated at the point in the vector space that corresponds to the input, $\mathbf{v}$. Hence $\mathbf{v} = v_1, v_2, \ldots, v_N$ gives rise to a set of numerical values $u_1(v_1, v_2, \ldots, v_K)$, $u_2(v_{K+1}, \ldots, v_e)$, $u_3(v_{e+1}, \ldots, v_m) \cdots u_s(v_r, \ldots, v_N)$. These values, $\mathbf{u} = (u_1, u_2, \ldots, u_s)$, represent the vector $\mathbf{v}$ in a vector space constructed of nonlinear discriminants, each operating on a different subgroup of the N variables. A nonlinear discriminant $y(\mathbf{u})$ can now be constructed to operate on the s-dimensional u-space. This procedure is often very useful when statistical independence of the subsets of variables can be reasonably well assured.

Nonlinear transformations also find uses in establishing a good assignment of coordinate values of subjective judgments used as dimensions of the vector space.

If little or nothing is known about the data, the adaptive sample set construction procedure is particularly useful. With it, an intuitive notion of the nature of the probability density of a given class can be gained. The number of modes of the probability density (the number of different clusters) can be estimated and their approximate locations can be determined relatively rapidly. Used as a completely automatic process of machine learning, it has resulted in low error probabilities even in the automatic recognition of classes where a significant number of the vectors were given as observed members of more than one class. In this case, no decision rule could make error-free decisions.

The desired result of applying automatic recognition of membership in classes is often the development of a special-purpose machine with which the decision rule can be implemented and classificatory decisions can be made rapidly. To keep the instrumentation simple and the decision rule physically interpretable, it is desirable to examine the generalized discriminant functions or probability densities to establish whether or not a better choice of the vector space were possible. Often a different choice of coordinates will simplify the probability densities of classes in the new vector space and will reduce the probability of error in decision making.

In the sections that follow, a few practical illustrations are given. We will start with an illustration of the use of linear discriminants and proceed to an example where Gaussian densities are fitted to the sets of samples. Nonlinear methods have been illustrated in Chapter III, while adaptive methods have been shown to be successful in recognizing the speaker regardless of the text he speaks.

5.4 RECOGNITION OF VOICED AND UNVOICED SPEECH SOUNDS

During voiced sounds speech power is concentrated in a few narrow bands of the frequency spectrum. These bands are called formants, as was pointed out in Chapter IV where a model of the human speech generating mechanism, valid during voiced sounds, was given. There we saw that the formant filters were excited by a pulse generator, during voiced sounds, while a noise generator supplied the excitation during the utterance of unvoiced sounds. Although a device for determining whether a sound is voiced or unvoiced should analyze speech to establish the method of excitation in the speech generating model, there are more easily instrumentable speech clues that machines can utilize in making satisfactory voiced-unvoiced decisions.

We can observe, on the sonagram of Fig. 4-4, that voiced sounds contain most of the power at the low frequencies while the power of unvoiced sounds is contained mostly at the higher frequencies. Experimental observations indicate that voiced sound energy lies mostly below about 1000 cps, while the power in unvoiced sound spectra is mostly contained in the region above 1000 cps. This fact has been utilized in speech analysis equipment, where the determination of voicing is accomplished with circuitry like that illustrated in Fig. 5-18. Here the amount of low-frequency power is compared with power at the higher frequencies by a comparison of the output amplitudes of two specially designed filters. The filter responses are qualitatively indicated in the diagram. After comparison with a fixed threshold, a binary output indicating the voiced-unvoiced decision is obtained.

A comparison of the high- and low-frequency power content of human speech sounds can be implemented in different ways. Speech analysis equipment of most widespread use (the Vocoder), for example, already contains a set of stagger-tuned bandpass filters that spans the spectrum

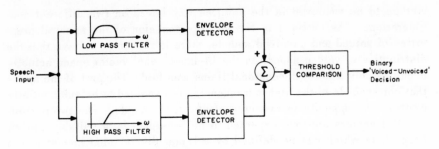

Figure 5-18. Conventional voiced-unvoiced decision.

of human speech and subdivides this spectrum into narrow bands of frequency. Any desired frequency response of the filters in the above diagram may be simulated by a linear combination of outputs of the bandpass
filters of the Vocoder. The implementation of this linear combination is
so simple that (having a Vocoder already) voiced-unvoiced decisions can
be made with a reduction in equipment complexity and with a possible improvement in the accuracy of voiced-unvoiced decisions.

The design of the optimum choice of linear weighting coefficients of
the Vocoder filter outputs to implement voiced-unvoiced decisions can
be made within the framework of a problem of pattern recognition. Each
sound is represented by a set of 18 numbers where each number denotes
the magnitude of the speech spectrum in one of 18 nonoverlapping bands
of frequency. An 18-channel Vocoder (a set of 18 stagger-tuned filters)
was used in this experiment. The envelope-detected filter outputs are
quantized to a range of 8 numerical values. The set of 18 octal numbers
thought of as an 18-dimensional vector represents the sound at a given
instant. A large number of voiced sounds are collected and converted to
a large number of 18-dimensional vectors. A large quantity of unvoiced
sounds are similarly represented.

The design of the network that weights the different Vocoder filter
outputs can be undertaken through the application of the linear class-
separating transformations discussed in Chapter II. We recall that a
direction in the vector space is found, through the application of those
methods, along which projections of voiced sounds are maximally separated from projections of unvoiced sounds, while projections of sounds
within each group are clustered close to each other. In a two-dimensional
illustration, this was portrayed in Fig. 2-8.

The solution of the problem of the recognition of voiced sounds and
their differentiation from unvoiced sounds fits well within the framework
of classificatory decision making in pattern recognition. Now let us set
about the task of choosing the dimensions and the samples in the vector
space. The vector space itself was already chosen from physical considerations based on prior knowledge of the problem to be solved, and the

method to be employed in the solution was based on two different considerations. As outlined in the above discussion of the spectral properties of voiced and unvoiced sounds, there is reason to believe that the distribution of voiced sounds in the 18-dimensional vector space actually occupies only a lower dimensional linear manifold. The part of the space that corresponds to the higher frequencies is expected to be substantially empty. The opposite is expected of unvoiced sounds. The two populations of vectors are thus expected to be separable by a suitably chosen hyperplane which can be defined by a linear discriminant normal to the plane, a vector of 18 dimensions.

The problem that remains to be solved is that of selecting samples on which voiced-unvoiced discrimination will be learned. The relative frequency of occurrence of sounds in the English language is given in a table by J. V. Tobias.* This table is based on the occurrence (per thousand sounds) of sounds in the English language. The number of different English sounds and the requirement that the number of samples on which we learn should exceed the number of dimensions of the space (or the number of coefficients we wish to determine) influences the choice of the number of samples. A total of about 240 samples were chosen, thus tending to assure the satisfaction of both of the above requirements. Since the ratio of voiced to unvoiced sounds is approximately 4:1, a sample size of approximately 189 voiced sounds and 51 unvoiced sounds was used. A sample set having the above properties was collected from a number of available speakers. Care was taken in the process of sample collection to assure the independence of samples. This was achieved by selecting only one sample from a single occurrence of a sound. Two adjacent samples from a single sound would have been less suitable, since statistical dependence of such samples would be expected.

A general purpose computer was programmed to execute the operations involved in the construction of the matrices U and D and in the solution of the matrix equation of Eq. (5.15).

$$\mathbf{w}(\mathbf{U} - \lambda\mathbf{D}) = 0 \qquad \text{where } \mathbf{D} = [\mathbf{m}(v) - \mathbf{m}(u)]^T [\mathbf{m}(v) - \mathbf{m}(u)]. \qquad (5.15)$$

The eigenvector $\mathbf{w}$ corresponding to the smallest λ defines the direction in the vector space along which the distance between projections of the means of the classes of voiced and unvoiced sounds is constant while the projection of distances between members of the same class are minimized. The matrix U is the sum of sample covariance matrices of voiced and voiced sounds, and matrix D is given in Eq. (5.15). The mean of voiced sounds is denoted by the vector $\mathbf{m}(v)$, while the mean of unvoiced sounds is denoted by $\mathbf{m}(u)$.

---

*J.A.S.A., **31**, 631, May, 1959.

The decision rule, the comparison of the distances between the 18-dimensional vector representation of a sound and the means of each of the two classes along the direction defined by the linear discriminant, **w**, can be expressed in a more suitable form. It can be equated to the evaluation of the correlation coefficient between the input and the vector w and to the comparison of the correlation coefficient with a threshold, T. This is shown in Eqs. (5.16) and (5.17), where v_n is the nth coordinate of the 18-dimensional vector that represents the sound, w_n is the weighting coefficient associated with the nth Vocoder channel, and T is the threshold of comparison. The decision rule, stated in Eq. (5.16) is equivalent to that given in Eq. (5.17).

Decide that **v** is voiced, if
$$\left(\sum_{n=1}^{18} w_n [v_n - m_n(v)] \right)^2 <$$
$$< \left(\sum_{n=1}^{18} w_n [v_n - m_n(u)] \right)^2. \qquad (5.16)$$

Decide that **v** is unvoiced, if
$$\sum_{n=1}^{18} w_n v_n > T =$$
$$= \sum_{n=1}^{18} \frac{w_n}{2} [m_n(v) + m_n(u)]. \qquad (5.17)$$

The decision rule of Eq. (5.17) can be implemented by the network shown in Fig. 5-19. In this network the Vocoder channel outputs are at-

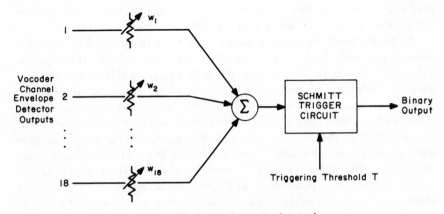

Figure 5-19. Voiced-unvoiced switch.

tenuated by an amount determined by the corresponding coordinate of the discriminant, and the attenuated channel outputs are summed, before comparison with a threshold T, in a Schmitt trigger circuit, which indicates an unvoiced decision if its input exceeds T.

When 18-dimensional vector representations of sounds of known classification (voiced or unvoiced) were subjected to machine classification by the decision rule of Eq. (5.17), 14 out of 189 voiced sounds and 2 out of 51 unvoiced sounds were misclassified. A total of 16 out of 240 or 6.6 per cent of the sounds were misclassified. Of the 16 errors, in six instances the vector representation of the input sounds was in error (probably due to errors in the analog-to-digital conversions of the Vocoder channel outputs) and in all remaining cases decision errors proved to be very marginal errors. A marginal error is one where the correlation coefficient expressed in Eq. (5.17) is only marginally greater (or smaller) than T.

5.5 AUTOMATIC RECOGNITION OF SPOKEN NUMERALS

Recognition of a spoken numeral is a problem in the recognition of membership in classes, classes which are known only from a set of their samples. A class is, for example, the "spoken word seven" regardless whether it is a man, woman, or child who speaks the word. A sample of this class is the particular utterance of the word "seven" by a specific person, while another sample is the utterance of the same word by someone else. We wish to design a method of processing sample occurrences of spoken numerals, so that, from the sets of samples, a decision procedure could be constructed which will classify every spoken word, regardless of who speaks it, as a member of one of the ten classes of words; that is, as an occurrence of a particular spoken numeral.

As in any instance where a physical problem is attacked by a mathematical approach, first the problem of constructing a model of the physical world must be faced. In classification problems this is synonymous with the selection of the vector space in which events must be represented as vectors. There are, of course, many ways of representing words with vectors. One method of representation is to sample the microphone output at the Nyquist rate and thus produce $2TW$ sample heights with which a word of length T and bandwidth W could be uniquely characterized. The sequence of $2TW$ sample heights defines a $2TW$-dimensional vector, or a point in a $2TW$-dimensional space, which uniquely represents a given spoken word. Several other vector spaces could be constructed. The particular choice made in this study was the representation of a word by its sonagraph, shown in Fig. 5-20, where frequency is shown along the ordinate and time along the abscissa. If an imaginary rectangular grid structure is superimposed on the sonagraph, the word can be represented by an array of numbers, each of which signifies the average intensity of the speech in the corresponding time-frequency cell. Such an array of numbers is shown in the figure directly below the sonagraph. Each one-digit number (between 0 and 7) signifies in octal form the average intensity of the speech during a given interval of time and within a given interval of frequency. If this array of numbers is read by scanning, as a television camera would read it, a sequence of octal numbers will be obtained which characterize the spoken word. The printout at the bottom of Fig. 5-20 was obtained actually by means of an 18-channel Vocoder. The envelope of each channel was sampled at the rate of one sample per 20 msec, with the result that a one-second portion of speech is represented as a point in a 900-dimensional space. Note that the samples are orthogonal by construction because they represent waveforms that are disjointed either in frequency or in time.

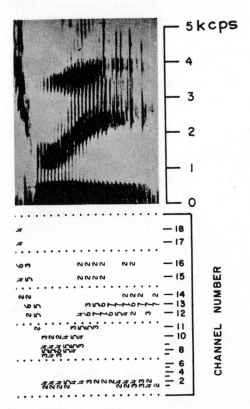

Figure 5-20. Sonagraph representation of the spoken word "three."

For convenience, words were normalized in duration to 0.4 second by taking an equal number of samples per word rather than by taking an equal number of samples per unit time.   The word-normalization time-scale factor was introduced as an additional dimension of the space, and this resulted in the representation of spoken utterances as points in a 361-dimensional space. (No special significance should be attached, however, to the number 361; it was merely a convenient choice.)

The method of representation described above is known to be sufficient to contain all the information needed to recognize words, since good quality human speech can be generated with this method of parametric speech representation. The word normalization scale factor serves two purposes. It fixes the number of dimensions of the space in which further computations must be performed, and it reduces variations of word representations that would result from speaker-to-speaker differences in talking rate. Word length normalization, on the other hand, does not affect the internal distribution of sounds. The relative duration of syllables and sounds within the word is not affected by the normalization.

From physical considerations there is reason to believe that, although the mean-square error between vector representations of words would not be a good measure of their similarity, a somewhat more general error criterion would serve well in the recognition of spoken words. Several factors justify this hypothesis. One, and by no means a trivial factor, is that equipment considerations demand the use of automatic gain control amplifiers in speech analysis equipment. Automatic gain control tends to normalize the total energy contained in each instantaneous spectrum and thus tends to normalize the energy contained in the entire word. Since the length of the vector in the above representation is approximately proportional to word energy, automatic gain control tends to normalize the length of the word vector. Actual measurements indicate that the vector magnitudes are within about 20 per cent of each other. Words are thus points within a spherical shell in the 361-dimensional space, where the shell thickness is about 1/5 of its radius. Numeral-to-numeral variations manifest themselves in the different angular directions in which word vectors are pointing and in the shape and orientation of the region in the wall of the spherical shell in which examples of the same word are contained.

Since the principal difference between different words is in the direction in which their representative vectors are pointing, one might think that correlation between a word and the mean vector of each of the numerals would suffice to recognize the word as a specific numeral. The fact, however, that all coordinates of the vector are always positive causes even dissimilar words to crowd together, since vectors with only positive coefficients lie in the first quadrant of the vector space. This fact necessitates that we take advantage of differences in the directions within the spherical shell in which members of a given class are distributed. Thus the choice of fitting different ellipsoidal regions (Gaussian probability densities) to each of the numerals was made as the method of recognizing spoken numerals.

An adequate number of sample words could not be collected to assure the nonsingularity of the covariance matrices. It seemed certain however, that a relatively few number of words of each class would suffice to learn the recognition of spoken digits. Four hundred different utterances by 10 male speakers with regional accents drawn from the Northeast corner of the United States were collected on magnetic tape. No attempt was made to control the speakers or their rate of speech. The recordings were converted to the numerical format shown in Fig. 5-20 with the aid of an 18-channel Vocoder. Word length was normalized by a computer that determined the beginning and the end of the word and fitted a set of 20 sampling instances between these two extremes. The available sample nearest the new sampling instances was retained to obtain a 360-dimensional vector. The vector space was augmented by the word length as the 361st dimension.

The effect of the number of sample utterances used in learning was investigated. First, M samples of each of the ten categories were selected as the labeled samples from which numeral recognition would be learned. At first, M was chosen three; later the computations were repeated with M gradually increasing to ten.

The first step in the process of finding the orthogonal transformations that minimize the mean-square distances between points of each of the categories is to find the orthonormal transformations that rotate the given coordinate system into the optimum one. Because this would involve solving for the eigenvalues and vectors of 361×361 matrices, at best a time consuming process, we use the knowledge that the eigenvectors of each solution will be contained in the M-dimensional linear manifold of the space spanned by the vectors of each set. The M vectors of each set were therefore orthogonalized to obtain ten M-dimensional coordinate systems in which the sample vectors of each set could be expressed in no more than M-dimensions.

The covariance matrices of each set of vectors were constructed, and the eigenvalues and eigenvectors of these matrices were obtained. All these computations were performed on a general-purpose digital computer. The eigenvectors of a covariance matrix form the columns of the rotation transformation C (Chapter II), while the reciprocals of the corresponding eigenvalues are the elements of the diagonal matrix W. The latter expresses the weighting associated with each new eigenvector. The eigenvectors were now expressed in the original 361-dimensional coordinate system, and the computation of the quadratic forms (exponents of the Gaussian probability densities) were programmed on the computer.

The decision regarding membership of an unknown speech event was determined by the quadratic form of smallest value. The a priori probabilities of the spoken digits were assumed equal.

Typical results which demonstrate improvement in the machine's performance as the number of known, labeled examples of spoken digits is increased, are illustrated in Fig. 5-21. This figure contains four con-

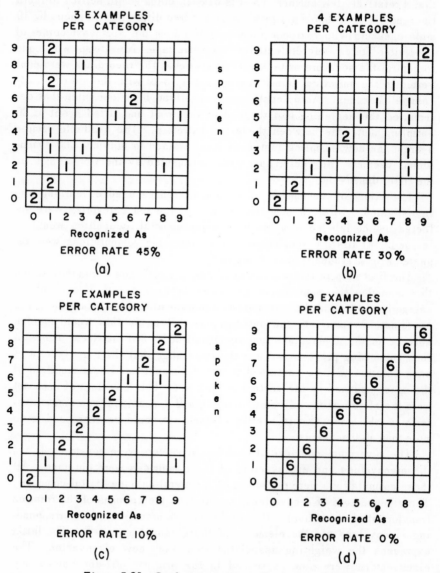

Figure 5-21. Confusion matrices illustrating spoken numeral recognition.

fusion matrices constructed for the cases where numeral recognition was learned from three, four, seven, and nine examples of each of the 10 categories of digits. The ordinate indicates the meaning of the word spoken by the talker during a test, while the abscissa indicates the decision rendered by the machine. The number in a cell of the confusion matrix indicates the number of different instances in which the same decision was made. For example, in Fig. 5-21a, the spoken word "seven" was recognized as "one" in two instances; that is, the machine made two errors. On the other hand, in one instance the spoken word "five" was recognized by the machine as a "five"; and in another instance as a "nine"; that is, the machine rendered one correct decision. When the machine's performance in recognizing spoken numerals is nearly perfect, numbers on the confusion matrix are arranged most nearly along the main diagonal, representing correct decisions. The number of examples of each of the numerals on which the machine based its decision of how to recognize spoken digits is shown above each example. For instance, when only three examples were given of each of the ten digits, the machine's performance was fairly poor, its error rate being 45 per cent. When the number of given samples was increased to four, the error rate dropped to 30 per cent; for seven samples, 10 per cent. When the number of known samples of the spoken digits reached nine, the machine made no errors. This result is particularly interesting in view of the fact that many of the spoken digits tested were spoken by people not included among those whose words were used as examples.

Using the same techniques, but enlarging the number of dimensions of the space in which spoken digits are represented, improved results may be obtained. The addition of parameters — considered useful from linguistic considerations — as new dimensions of the vector space would further increase the clusterability of words of the same category.

BIBLIOGRAPHY

Ashby, W. Ross. *Design for a Brain.* New York: John Wiley & Sons, Inc.; London: Chapman & Hall, Ltd., 1952.

Baran, P. and Estrin, G. "An Adaptive Character Reader," IRE WESCON *Convention Record,* Part 4, 29–41 (1960).

Bar-Hillel, Y. "Can Translation be Mechanized?" *American Scientist,* 42, 248–60 (April 1954).

———. "Linguistic Problems Connected with Machine Translation," British Journal for the Philosophy of Science, 20, No. 3, 217–25 (July 1953).

Bernstein, A., *et al.* "A Chess Playing Program for the IBM 704," *Proceedings of the Western Joint Computer Conference,* pp. 157–59 (May 6–8, 1958).

Bledsoe, W. W., and Browning, I. "Pattern Recognition and Reading by Machine," *Proceedings of the Eastern Joint Computer Conference,* pp. 225–32 (December 1959).

Bomba, J. S. "Alpha-Numeric Character Recognition Using Local Operations." Paper presented at the Eastern Joint Computer Conference (December 3, 1959).

Bremer, R. W. "A Checklist of Intelligence for Programming Systems," *Communications of the Association for Computing Machinery,* 2, 8–13 (March 1959).

Carr, J. W. "Recursive Subscripting Compilers and List-Type Memories," *Communications of the Association for Computing Machinery,* 2, 4–6 (February 1959).

Chow, C. K. "An Optimum Character-Recognition System Using Decision Functions," *IRE Transactions on Electronic Computers,* EC-6, 247–54 (December 1957).

Clark, W. A., and Farley, B. G. "Generalizations of Pattern Recognition in a Self-Organizing System," *Proceedings of the Western Joint Computer Conference* (1955).

Daphne, J. Innes. "Filter—A Topological Pattern-Separation Computer Program," *Proceedings of the Eastern Joint Computer Conference,* pp. 25–37 (December 1960).

David, Jr., E. E. "Artificial Auditory Recognition in Telephony," *IBM Journal of Research and Development,* 2, No. 4 (1958).

———, and McDonald, H. S. "A Bit-Squeezing Technique Applied to Speech Signals," *IRE Convention Record,* pp. 148–52 (1956).

Denes, P. "The Design and Operation of the Mechanical Speech Recognizer," and "Discussion," Journal of British IRE, 19, 219–34 (April 1959).

Dimond, T. L. "Devices for Reading Handwritten Characters," *Proceedings of Eastern Joint Computer Conference*, pp. 232–37 (1957).

Dinneen, G. P. "Programming Pattern Recognition," *Proceedings of the Western Joint Computer Conference* (March 1955).

Doyle, W. "Recognition of Sloppy, Hand-printed Characters," *Proc. Western Joint Computer Conference*, pp. 133–42 (May 1960).

Dunker, K. "On Problem Solving," *Psychological Monographs*, **58**, No. 270 (1945).

Evey, R. J. "Use of a Computer to Design Character Recognition Logic." Paper presented at Eastern Joint Computer Conference (December 1959).

Fatehchand, R. "Machine Recognition of Spoken Words," in *Advances in Computers*, **1**, 207, New York: Academic Press, 1960.

Feldman, J. "A Theory of Binary Choice Behavior," CIP Working Paper No. 12, Carnegie Institute of Technology (May 1958).

Flores, I. "An Optimum Character Recognition System Using Decision Functions," *IRE Transactions on Electronic Computers*, EC-7, 180 (June 1958).

————, and Grey, L. "Optimization of Reference Signals for Character Recognition Systems," *IRE Transactions on Electronic Computers*, EC-9, 54–61 (March 1960).

Friedberg, R. M. "A Learning Machine," Part I, *IBM Journal of Research and Development*, 2 (January 1958).

Fuchs, W. "On Mathematical Analysis of Style," *Biometrika*, **39**, 122 (1952).

Galanter, Eugene, H. "The Behavior of Thought." Paper presented at the American Psychological Association Meeting in Chicago (1956).

Gardner, M. *Logic Machines and Diagrams*, New York: McGraw-Hill Book Company, Inc., 1958.

Gelernter, H. L., and Rochester, N. "Intelligent Behavior in Problem-Solving Machines," *IBM Journal of Research and Development*, 2, No. 4 (October 1958).

Gentzen, Gerhard. "Untersuchungen über das logische Schliessem," *Mathematische Zeitschrift*, **39** 176–210; 405–31 (1934).

Gill, A. "Mimimum-scan Pattern Recognition," *IRE Transactions on Information Theory*, IT-5, 52–8 (June 1959).

Glantz, H. T. "On the Recognition of Information with a Digital Computer," *Journal of the Association for Computing Machinery* (April 1957).

Gold, B. "Machine Recognition of Hand-Sent Morse Code," *IRE Transactions on Information Theory*, IT-5, 17–24 (March 1950).

Greanias, E. C., *et al.* "Design of Logics for Recognition of Printed Characters by Simulation," *IBM Journal of Research and Development*, **1**, 8–18 (January 1957).

Green, P. H. "Networks for Pattern Perception," *Proc. National Electronics Conference,* **15,** 357–69 (October 1959).

Grimsdale, R. L., *et al.* "A System for the Automatic Recognition of Patterns," *Journal of the Institution of Electrical Engineers, London,* **106,** Part B, 210–21 (March 1959).

Harmon, L. D. "A Line-drawing Pattern Recognizer," *Proc. Western Joint Computer Conference,* pp. 351–64 (May 1960).

Harris, Robert T., and **Jarrett, J. L.** *Language and Informal Logic.* New York: Longmans, Green & Co., Inc. (1956).

Hawkins, J. K. "Self Organizing Systems—A Review and Commentary," *Proc. IRE,* **49,** 31–48 (January 1961).

Hebb, D. O. *The Organization of Behavior.* New York: John Wiley & Sons, Inc.; London: Chapman & Hall, Ltd. (1949).

Hilgard, E. *Theories of Learning.* 2nd ed. New York: Appleton-Century-Crofts, Inc., 1956.

Horwitz, L. P., and **Shelton, G. L.** "Pattern Recognition Using Autocorrelation," *Proc. IRE,* **49,** 175–85 (January 1961).

Hovland, C. I. "A Communication Analysis of Concept Learning," *Psychological Review,* **59** (1952).

Humphrey, G. *Thinking.* New York: John Wiley & Sons, Inc., 1951.

Ianov, IU. I. "On the Equivalence and Transformation of Program Schemes," *Doklady Akademii Nauk S.S.S.R.,* **113,** No. 1 (1957).

———. "On Matrix Program Schemes," *Doklady Akademii Nauk S.S.S.R.,* **113,** No. 2 (1957). Also published in *Communications of the Association of Computer Machinery,* **1,** No. 12 (December 1958).

Kamentsky, L. A. "Pattern and Character Recognition Systems—Picture Processing by Nets of Neuron-like Elements," *Proc. Western Joint Computer Conference,* pp. 304–309 (May 1959).

Kirsch, L. C., *et al.* "Experiments in Processing Pictorial Information with a Digital Computer," *Proceedings of the Eastern Joint Computer Conference,* pp. 221–30 (December 1957).

Kister, J., *et al.* "Experiments in Chess," *Journal of the Association for Computing Machinery,* **4,** 2 (April 1957).

Kramer, H. P., and **Mathews, M. V.** "A Linear Coding for Transmitting a Set of Correlated Signals," *IRE* Transactions on Information Theory, IT-2 (September 1956). Paper presented at Symposium on Information Theory held at MIT, September 10–12, 1956.

Kretzmer, E. R. "Reduced Alphabet Representation of Television Signals," *IRE Convention Record,* Information Theory section, Part 4, p. 140 (1956).

Lambek, J. "The Mathematics of Sentence Structure," *American Mathematical Monthly,* **65** (March 3, 1958).

Lashley, K. S. *Cerebral Mechanism in Behavior.* New York: John Wiley & Sons, Inc., 1951.

Latil, de P. *Thinking by Machine.* Boston: Houghton Mifflin Company, 1956.

Levin, K. *Principles of Topological Psychology.* New York: McGraw-Hill Book Company, Inc., 1936.

Locke, W. N., and Booth, A. D. *Machine Translation of Languages.* New York: John Wiley & Sons, Inc., 1955.

Luchins, A. S. "Mechanization in Problem Solving," *Psychological Monographs,* **54**, No. 6 (1942).

Luhn, H. "The Automatic Creation of Literature Abstracts," *IBM Journal of Research and Development,* **2**, No. 2 (April 1958).

Marill, T., and Green, D. M. "Statistical Recognition Functions and the Design of Pattern Recognizers," *IRE Transactions on Electronic Computers,* EC–9, 472–77 (December 1960).

Mattson, Richard L. "A Self Organizing Logical System," Paper presented at the Eastern Joint Computer Conference (December 3, 1959).

McCarthy, J., in C. E. Shannon and J. McCarthy (eds.). *Automata Studies.* Princeton, New Jersey: Princeton University Press, 1956.

McCulloch, W. S., and Pitts, W. "A Logical Calculus of the Ideas Imminent in Nervous Activity," *Bulletin of Mathematical Biophysics,* **9**, (1947).

————, *et al.* "Symposium on the Design of Machines to Simulate the Behavior of the Human Brain," *IRE Transactions on Electronic Computers,* EC–5, No. 4 (December 1956).

Miller, G. A. *Language and Communication.* New York: McGraw-Hill Book Company, Inc., 1951.

————. "The Magical Number Seven," *Psychological Review,* **63** (1956).

————, and Selfridge, J. A. "Verbal Context and the Recall of Meaningful Material," *American Journal of Psychology,* **63** (1946).

Minsky, Marvin L. "Exploration Systems and Syntactic Processes," (unpublished report), Summer Research Project on Artificial Intelligence, Dartmouth College, New Hampshire (1956).

————. "Heuristic Aspects of the Artificial Intelligence Problem," Group Report 34–35, Lincoln Lab., MIT, (December 17, 1956).

Moore, O. K., and Anderson, S. B. "Modern Logic and Tasks for Experiments on Problem Solving Behavior," *Journal of Psychology,* **38**, 151–60 (1954).

More, Jr., Trenchard. "Deductive Logic for Automata." Unpublished Master's thesis (Massachusetts Institute of Technology, 1957).

Morris, Charles. *Signs, Language and Behavior,* New York: Prentice-Hall, Inc., 1946.

Neumann, J. von. "The General and Logical Theory of Automata," in *Cerebral Mechanism in Behavior,* Jeffress (ed.), New York: John Wiley & Sons, Inc., 1951.

————. *Theory of Games and Economic Behavior.* Princeton, New Jersey: Princeton University Press, 1947.

Newell, A. "The Chess Machine," *Proceedings of the Western Joint Computer Conference* (March 1955).

Newell, A., Shaw, J. C., and Simon, H. A. "Elements of a Theory of Human Problem Solving," the Rand Corporation Report No. P–971, Santa Monica, Calif. (March 4, 1957).

――――. "Chess-Playing Programs and the Problem of Complexity," *IBM Journal of Research and Development*, **2**, No. 4, 320–35 (October 1958).

――――. "The Elements of a Theory of Human Problem Solving," *Psychological Review*, **65** (March, 1958).

――――. "Empirical Exploration of the Logic Theory Machine," *Proceedings of the Western Joint Computer Conference* (February 1957).

――――. "Empirical Exploration of the Logic Theory Machine," (rev.), The Rand Corporation Report No. P–951 Santa Monica, Calif. (March 14, 1957).

――――. "General Problem Solving Program," CIP Working Paper No. 7, Carnegie Institute of Technology (December 1957).

――――. "The Processes of Creative Thinking," The Rand Corporation Report No. P–1320 (August 1958).

――――. "Report on a General Problem Solving Program," The Rand Corporation Report No. P–1584 (January 1959).

――――, and Shaw, J. C. "Programming the Logic Theory Machine," *Proceedings of the Western Joint Computer Conference* (February 1957).

――――. "Programming the Logic Theory Machine" (revised), The Rand Corporation Report No. P–954, Santa Monica, Calif. (February 28, 1957).

――――, and Simon, H. A. "Current Developments in Complex Information Processing," The Rand Corporation Report No. P–850, Santa Monica, Calif. (May 1, 1956).

――――. "The Logic Theory Machine," *IRE Transactions on Information Theory*, IT–**2**, 61–79 (September 1956).

――――. "The Logic Theory Machine. A Complex Information Processing System" (revised), The Rand Corporation Report No. P–868, Santa Monica, Calif. (July 12, 1956).

Oettinger, A. G. "Simple Learning by a Digital Computer," *Proceedings of the Association for Computing Machinery* (September 1952).

Perry, J. W., Kent, A., and Berry, N. M. *Machine Literature Searching*, New York: Interscience Publishers, Inc., 1956.

Petrick, S. R. and Willett, H. M. "A Method of Voice Communication with a Digital Computer," *Proc. Eastern Joint Computer Conference*, pp. 11–24 (December 13–15, 1960).

Pitts, W., and McCulloch, W. S. "How We Know Universals, the Perception of Auditory and Visual Form," *Bulletin Mathematical Biophysics*, **9** (1947).

Polya, G. *How to Solve It,* Princeton, New Jersey: Princeton University Press, 1945.

———. *Mathematics and Plausible Reasoning.* Vols. I, II, Princeton, New Jersey: Princeton University Press, 1954.

Rapaport, D. *The Organization and Pathology of Thought.* New York: Columbia University Press, 1951.

Rochester, N., *et al.* "Tests on a Cell Assembly Theory of the Action of the Brain Using a Large Digital Computer," *IRE Transactions on Information Theory,* IT-**2**, No. 3 (September 1956).

Rosenblatt, F. "The Perceptron: A Probabilistic Model for Information Storage and Organization in the Brain," *Psychological Review,* **65**, No. 6 (November 1958).

———. "The Perceptron, A Theory of Statistical Separability in Cognitive Systems," Cornell Aeronautical Laboratory, Project PARA, Report No. VG-1196-G-1 (January 1958).

Sebestyen, G. S. "Recognition of Membership in Classes," *IRE Transactions on Information Theory,* IT-**6**, 44–50 (January 1961).

———. "Classification Decisions in Pattern Recognition," Technical Report 381, Research Laboratory of Electronics of Massachusetts Institute of Technology (April 1960).

Selfridge, Oliver G. "Pandemonium: A Paradigm for Learning," *Proceedings of the Symposium on Mechanization of Thought Processes,* held at the National Physical Laboratory, Teddington, Middlesex, England (November 24–27, 1958).

———. "Pattern Recognition and Learning," *Symposium on Information Theory,* London, England (1955). Preprinted Group Report 34–43, Lincoln Laboratory of Massachusetts Institute of Technology (July 20, 1955).

———. "Pattern Recognition and Modern Computers," *Proceedings of the Western Joint Computer Conference,* pp. 91–93 (March 1955).

———, *et al.* "Pattern Recognition and Reading by Machine," *Proceedings of the Eastern Joint Computer Conference* (December 3, 1959).

Shannon, Claude E. "Communication Theory of Secrecy Systems," *Bell System Technical Journal,* **28**, 656–715 (1949).

———. "Computers and Automata," *Proceedings of the IRE,* **41** (March 1950).

———. "A Mathematical Theory of Communication," *Bell System Technical Journal,* **27**, 379–423 (October 1948).

———. "Prediction and Entropy of Printed English" *Bell System Technical Journal,* **30**, 50–64 (1951).

———. "Programming a Computer for Playing Chess," *The Philosophical Magazine,* Vol. 41 (March 1950).

———. "The Rate of Approach to Ideal Coding," *IRE National Convention Record,* Part 4 (Abstract pages only) (1955).

————. "Automata Studies," *Annals of Mathematics Studies*, J. Mc-
Carthy (ed.). No. 4, Princeton (1956).

Shaw, J. C. *et al.* "A Command Structure for Complex Information
Processing," *Proceedings of the Western Joint Computer Conference*
(May 1958).

Simon, H. A. "A Behavioral Model of Rational Choice," *The Quarterly
Journal of Economics*, Vol. 69 (February 1955).

————. "Rational Choice and the Difficulty of the Environment,"
Psychological Review, Vol. 63 (March 1956).

————, **and Newell, A.** "Models: Their Uses and Limitations," *The
State of Social Sciences*, White (ed.). University of Chicago (1956).

Simons, Leo, "New Axiomatizations of S3 and S4," *Journal of Symbolic
Logic*, **18**, No. 4, 309–16 (1953).

Solomonoff, R. J. "An Inductive Inference Machine" (privately circulated
report) (August 14, 1956); *IRE National Convention Record*, Vol. 5,
and Part 2, pp. 56–62 (1957); *Annals of Mathematical Studies*, No.
34, Princeton (1956).

————. "A New Method for Discovering the Grammars of Phase Structure Languages," AFOSR TN–59–110, under Contract No. AF49(638)–
376 (April 1959) (ASTIA AD No. 210 390).

————. "The Mechanization of Linguistic Learning," AFOSR-TN–246
under Contract No. AF49(638)–376 (April 1959) (ASTIA AD No. 212
226).

Stearns, S. D. "A Method for the Design of Pattern Recognition Logic,"
IRE Transactions on Electronic Computers, EC-**9**, 48–53 (March
1960).

Steinbuch, K. "Automatic Speech Recognition," *Nachrichtentechnische
Zeitschrift*, **11**, 446–54 (September 1958).

Strachey, C. S. "Logical or Non-Mathematical Programs," *Proceedings
of the Association for Computing Machinery* (September 1952).

Taylor, W. K. "Pattern Recognition by Means of Automatic Analogue
Apparatus," *Proceedings of the IRE, (London)*, Vol. 106, Part B,
pp. 198–209 (March 1959).

Tersoff, A. I. "Electronic Reader Sorts Mail," *Electronic Industries*,
pp. 56–60 (July 1958).

Turing, A. M. "Can a Machine Think?" in *The World of Mathematics*,
J. R. Newman (ed.). Vol. IV. New York: Simon and Schuster, Inc.
1956.

————, "On Computable Numbers," *Proceedings of the London Mathematical Society*, Series 2, Vol. 42 (1936–37). *See also* correction,
Ibid, Vol. 43 (1937).

Unger, S. H. "A Computer Oriented Toward Spatial Problems," *Proceedings of the IRE*, **46**, 1744–50 (October 1958).

————. "Pattern Detection and Recognition," *Proceedings of the IRE*, **47**, No. 10, 1737 (October 1959).

Uttley, A. M. "The Classification of Signals in the Nervous System," *Radar Research Establishment Memorandum 1047*, Great Malvern, England (1954). Also published in the *Journal of Electroencephalography and Clinical Neurophysiology*, **6**, 479 (1954).

————. "The Probability of Neural Connections," *Radar Research Establishment Memorandum 1048*, Great Malvern, England (1954).

————. "Imitation of Pattern Recognition and Trial-and-Error Learning in a Conditional Probability Computer," *Revs. Mod. Phys.*, **31**, 546–48 (April 1959).

Yngve, V. "Programming Language for Mechanical Translation," *Mechanical Translation*, **5**, No. 1 (July 1958).

INDEX

adaptive
  classification, 90, 108
  sample selection, 99
algorithmic
  decision rule, 90, 93, 97
  discriminant, 85
approximation
  of decision regions, 90
  of generalized discriminant, 66
Bayes, 32, 63
Bionics, 108
calculus of variation, 67
cascaded machines, 112
character recognition, 1
classification, 4, 30, 61
class membership, 2
clustering, 9, 11, 30, 57, 63, 111
communications theory, 5
convex region, 129
correlation, 55, 111, 115, 119
cost, 31, 88
covariance matrix, 25, 131
decision
  region, 12, 91
  rule, 10, 30, 63, 75, 91
  theory, 4, 30
Dimond, T., 2
discriminant, 6, 15
  linear, 39, 95, 126, 129, 131
  generalized nonlinear, 61, 132
dot product, 111, 119, 127
eigenvalue, 28, 41, 61, 131
eigenvector, 25, 61, 131
error
  expected, 64
  probability, 4, 12, 13, 107
Euclidean distance, 19, 36, 57, 92, 120
false alarm, 30

false dismissal, 30
feature weighting, 17
forgetting, 50
formant, 94, 134
function of the vector space, 62, 132
Gaussian, 6, 33, 34, 63, 82, 88, 100, 129, 134
geometrical interpretation, 54, 61, 131
hyperplane, 115
incomplete variables, 74
interset distance, 38, 40, 43
intraset distance, 38, 43
invariance, 61, 131
inverse matrix, 34
labeled samples, 39, 47, 103, 111
Lagrange multiplier, 27, 59, 61, 63
likelihood ratio, 15, 76, 97
  average, 77
  maximum, 15
  most probable, 77
linear
  discriminants, 39, 95, 126, 129, 131
  machines, 111
  manifold, 78
  methods, 55
  transformations, 24
machine learning, 33, 47, 100, 103
majority rule, 97
mapping, 58, 136
marginal density, 76, 80, 89, 93
matrix
  covariance, 25, 131
  inverse, 34
  orthogonal, 34
  singular, 28, 42, 131
maximization, 38, 43

mean
  ensemble, 6, 35
  square distance, 15
  square error, 55
metric, 10, 16
minimization, 17, 43
model (mathematical), 8, 11, 56
moments, 23, 67
multipath, 21
multiply-connected, 90, 94
multivariate random process, 5
neural nets, 108
noise, 6, 32, 80
nonlinear
  methods, 54, 113
  transformations, 57
orthonormal transformation, 34
partitioning, 9, 13, 29, 90
pattern
  detection, 2
  recognition, 2, 4
Perceptron, 6, 108
pitch, 94
polynomial approximation, 67
prediction, 77
probability
  density, 6, 63
  of error, 4, 12, 13, 107
  of false alarm, 30

  of false dismissal, 30
projection, 42
properties, 8, 131
proximity algorithm, 91, 93
recognition, 33, 61, 80
regression, 121, 125
sample set, 9, 61, 63, 98
selective sampling, 98
similarity, 12, 29
simply-connected, 111, 129
speaker recognition, 1, 93, 104
speech recognition, 1, 139
statistical hypothesis testing, 4
storage limitation, 6, 98
subjective measurements, 134
supervised learning, 49
surface, 14, 62, 132
template, 10
threat evaluation, 1
threshold, 32, 48, 51, 121
transformations, 6, 10, 19, 57
truth table, 2
typical samples, 91, 103, 116
Unger, S.H., 2
unsupervised learning, 49
variance, 6, 100
vector space, 5, 8, 62, 140
voiced-unvoiced, 6, 93, 142
word recognition, 62, 139, 146

DATE DUE

GAYLORD M-2			PRINTED IN U.S.A.